AF865128

1. *Leiurus quinquestriatus*

2. *Buthotus judaicus*

3. *Orthochirus scrobiculosus*

4. *Nebo hierichonticus*

With compliments

G. Levy

Jerusalem
July 1981

dC5020
#95

PUBLICATIONS OF THE ISRAEL ACADEMY
OF SCIENCES AND HUMANITIES

SECTION OF SCIENCES

FAUNA PALAESTINA

ARACHNIDA I: SCORPIONES

FAUNA PALAESTINA • ARACHNIDA I

SCORPIONES

by

G. LEVY and P. AMITAI

Jerusalem 1980

The Israel Academy of Sciences and Humanities

© The Israel Academy of Sciences and Humanities, 1980

Authors' Address:
Department of Zoology
The Hebrew University, Jerusalem, Israel

ISBN 965–208–013–6
ISBN 965–208–016–0

Printed in Israel
at Keterpress, Jerusalem

CONTENTS

PREFACE

This survey of the fauna of scorpions of Israel and Sinai was carried out over several years. All collecting methods were used, including ultraviolet lamps which render scorpions visible at night. With these lamps, large numbers of scorpions were collected in places where usually only a few specimens had previously been found. Dense populations were discovered in sand dunes, inland and in the Coastal Plain, places where scorpions are found very rarely. Included among these were species of *Buthacus*, which had not been known from these areas previously.

A study was also made (G. L.) of material from Asia and Africa in the Muséum National d'Histoire Naturelle, Paris, and the British Museum (Natural History), London. Several new species were then described and the systematic position of others was determined (Levy et al., 1973).

All species (except for one) which had been previously described from Israel and Sinai were found again. *Buthus voelschowi* Werner, 1902, described from Israel, cannot be identified with certainty (see also Levy et al., 1970). Werner's description does not agree with any species of the thousands of specimens examined, and we thus doubt the correctness of the locality he indicated.

Specimens are preserved in the collection of the Hebrew University, Jerusalem; catalogue numbers are preceded by the letters Sc. (=scorpion).

The mode of describing scorpions used by Vachon (1948–1951) is generally followed here. The paraxial organs of the males and the arrangement of the trichobothria are referred to only in figures. All scale-lines given in figures represent 1 mm. Geographical records for each species are indicated on the Distribution Maps. For place names, see the map at the end of the book. References of previous records from Israel and adjacent countries are summarized in a table in the Appendix on Distribution.

The spelling of geographical names is according to the *Oxford University Atlas*; of localities in Israel and Sinai, according to the maps published by the Survey of Israel.

ACKNOWLEDGEMENTS

This study is dedicated to Prof. A. Shulov, who studied Arachnida in this country for over forty years and without whose inspiration this work could not have been either undertaken or completed.

Sincere thanks for hospitality and help are expressed to Prof. M. Vachon, Muséum National d'Histoire Naturelle, Paris, and to Dr G.J. Sheals and the late Mr D.J. Clark, British Museum (Natural History), London. The survey was supported in part by the Fauna Palaestina Committee of the Israel Academy of Sciences and Humanities. We wish to thank Prof. G. Haas, Zoology Department, the Hebrew University of Jerusalem, and Prof. O. Theodor, Department of Parasitology, Medical School of the Hebrew University, for lending us important papers as well as scorpions from their collections. We are indebted to the staff of the Zoology Department, Tel Aviv University, and to the staff of the 'Beit Gordon' Museum at Kibbutz Degania 'A' for placing their collections at our disposal. We are grateful to G. Tsabar, S. Reichenstein, A. Haim, A. Shachnai, the late H. Zinner, J. Gershoni and J. Heller for valuable material. Advice on preparing distribution maps was kindly provided by Prof. Y.L. Werner, Zoology Department, Hebrew University. Prof. H.W. Levi, Museum of Comparative Zoology, Harvard University, and Prof. O. Theodor read drafts of the manuscript and offered helpful suggestions. Our sincere thanks for the drawings are extended to Mr. S. Schäfer (shaded figures) and to Ms S. Halbreich, for Figs. 1–24 and the line drawings. The photographs in the colour plate have been provided by J. Gershoni and P. Amitai. We also thank H. Hardin for her editorial assistance and N. Schneider of the Publication Department of the Israel Academy for overseeing the editing and production of this work.

INTRODUCTION

Zoogeography

Scorpion species of three families, Buthidae, Scorpionidae and Diplocentridae, are represented in the region under consideration. Nine genera with 19 species and subspecies were found. Three faunal elements, eremic, Mediterranean and Central Asian, are represented in this area. The majority of our species are eremic. They are found in the Coastal Plain, Sinai and the southern parts of Israel. Some species, such as *Androctonus australis, A. bicolor, Compsobuthus werneri werneri* and *Buthacus arenicola*, reach their northern border of distribution here. Other species, e.g. *Buthotus judaicus, Compsobuthus werneri judaicus* and *Scorpio maurus fuscus,* which occur only in the north and central parts of Israel, are Mediterranean elements. The Asian element is represented by *Androctonus crassicauda* and *Orthochirus scrobiculosus,* which reach their western border of distribution in our area. The distribution of *Nebo hierichonticus* in the Mediterranean zone of Israel and in the deserts of Sinai and southern Arabia is rather peculiar, and this is probably a relict of a more northern fauna. The exact distribution of *Butacus yotvatensis* and *Compsobuthus longipalpis* is not known; the latter may be an Ethiopian element.

Ecology and Biology

Many species of scorpions are found on a wide variety of types of soil, some on only a few types of soil. *Buthus, Androctonus bicolor, A. amoreuxi* and all the species of *Buthacus* occur on coastal sand dunes and sandy soil, while others, e.g. *A. crassicauda, Leiurus, Buthotus, Compsobuthus w. judaicus, Scorpio m. fuscus* and *Nebo,* are found on terra rossa, basalt and rendzina. Species of *Buthus, Leiurus, Compsobuthus w. werneri, Orthochirus, Scorpio m. palmatus* and *Nebo* are found in the stony desert, and some also on loess-like soil. Most of our species live under large or small stones, or sometimes in stone walls and rock crevices; some occasionally inhabit empty burrows of rodents or Isopoda. *Buthotus* and *Compsobuthus w. judaicus* are sometimes found under bark of trees. *Leiurus* and *Buthotus* sometimes enter houses. *Scorpio* and *Nebo* dig deep burrows, while others, e.g. *Leiurus,* dig shelters only slightly oblique to the surface of the ground. Hundreds of burrows of *Scorpio m. palmatus* may be concentrated on certain hillsides. Scorpions usually live alone, but *Compsobuthus w. judaicus* is sometimes found in winter in aggregations of over a dozen specimens under the same stone.

When running, scorpions usually hold the pedipalps ahead, apparently orienting themselves with the aid of the trichobothria, which are sensitive to air currents; the metasoma may be arched high above the back or, as in *Orthochirus,* pressed to the back in a curled position with the stinger completely hidden. In *Compsobuthus* the metasoma is usually curved laterally.

The period of activity extends throughout the warm season, but occasionally scorpions are also active on warm winter nights. Activity on nights with a full moon is restricted or absent. Diurnal activity occurs occasionally in early spring or after the first autumn rains at the sudden appearance of numerous insects and other arthropods which constitute their food. Predation usually takes place on the ground or on tree bark, and on bushes (even by burrowing species). Small prey is usually handled by the pedipalps alone, but may be stung if it struggles; the chelicerae then tear the food apart and the juices are sucked. Water is taken by crouching over a drop or with the drop being held between the fingers of one pedipalp and then brought to the mouth. Drops of dew may be sucked directly from plants with the chelicerae. Excrement is deposited on surrounding objects, rarely on the ground.

The males are usually more slender and may have a larger number of denticles on the pectines. The spermatophore is formed in the paraxial organs. The sclerotized inside of the paraxial organs provides a systematic character of specific importance in males (Fig. 29).

The details of courtship differ in various genera. Generally, however, the male approaches the female, whose pedipalps it may grasp with one or both of its own, while the metasoma of both may be held vertical and jerking. The pair then moves back and forth, and when a suitable firm surface is found the male deposits the spermatophore. The female is then manoeuvred into position with the genital opening above the spermatophore. Courtship and parturition generally take place in the warmer season (mostly in July and August). In the Buthidae of our area the young are born in an embryonic envelope from which they emerge within several minutes of birth. In *Scorpio* and *Nebo* the young are born without an envelope and soon ascend onto the mother's back. The young of burrowing species remain with the mother longer than those of other species.

Predators of scorpions are nocturnal birds (*Athene, Otus*), hedgehogs, snakes (*Eirenis*), skinks and lizards (some of which are not affected by the scorpion's sting), solifuges, spiders (*Latrodectus*), as well as other scorpions.

The sting of many scorpions is painful but is usually not dangerous. Two species in our area, *Leiurus quinquestriatus* and *Androctonus crassicauda* (rarely), may cause death to human beings. Specific antiserum against *L. quinquestriatus* is produced in Israel. There has been no record of fatalities due to *Androctonus australis* in Israel, although this species causes death in North Africa.

The lethal potency of the venom of certain buthid scorpions may be rated among the most virulent to mammals (Zlotkin, 1973). The sting of *L. quinquestriatus* is followed by sharp pain, restlessness, excessive salivation, lacrymation and accelerated respiration. Muscular convulsions and paralysis may ensue; death is due to respiratory or heart failure (Gueron & Yarom, 1970; for general information, see Efrati, 1978).

There are hardly any enzymes in the buthid venoms (Balozet, 1971). The toxicity of these venoms to mammals is due to low-molecular-weight basic proteins with neurotoxic action (for further information see Zlotkin at al., 1978). Over twenty different toxic proteins have been isolated from buthid venoms. Most of these are active against mammals; others are specific against insects or isopods (Zlotkin, 1973). Considering the scorpion's biology, toxicity against arthropods appears to be of great importance.

The venom of the Scorpionidae and Diplocentridae is less toxic to mammals than that of the Buthidae (Zlotkin et al., 1972; Rosin, 1969). The sting of *Nebo* (Diplocentridae) causes local hemorrhages and necrosis in mice, thus indicating toxins of a different nature (Rosin, 1969). The venom of *Scorpio m. palmatus* is apparently much more toxic to insects than to mice (Zlotkin et al., 1972). Possibly, the venom of each scorpion family contains different toxins.

Morphology

The body of the scorpion consists of two main parts which are broadly connected: the *prosoma* (cephalothorax) and the *opisthosoma.* The latter consists of a wide anterior *mesosoma* and a slender posterior *metasoma* which bears the stinger containing the venom glands.

The prosoma is covered by an unsegmented carapace with a pair of median eyes near the middle and a group of two to five lateral eyes on each side; some cave-dwelling species are blind. Surface structures of the carapace, such as crests (keels), grooves, granules, etc. (Fig. 1), are important diagnostic generic characters. The appendages of the prosoma consist of the *chelicerae,* the pedipalps armed with large pincers and

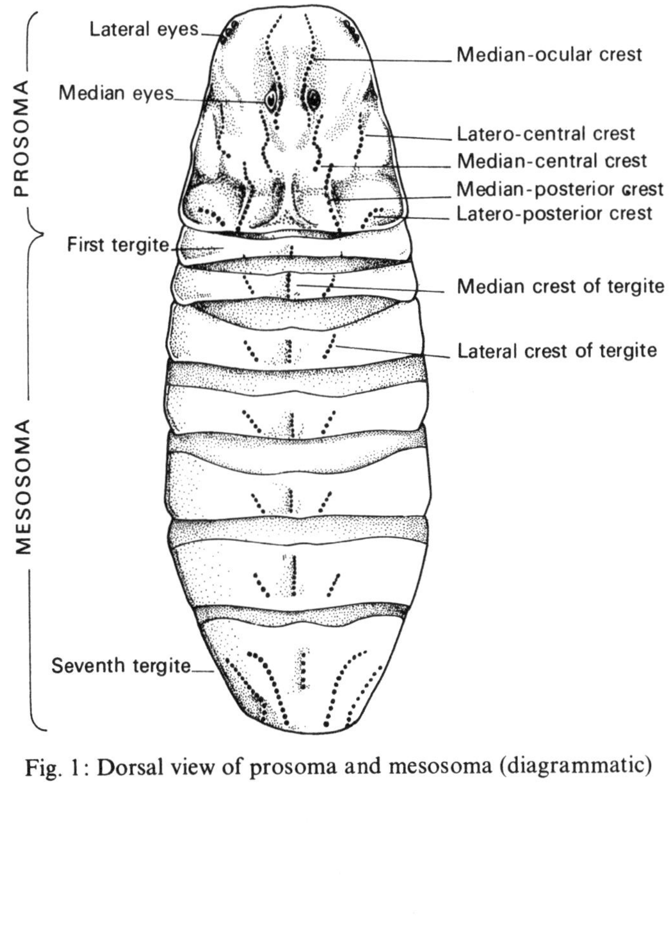

Fig. 1: Dorsal view of prosoma and mesosoma (diagrammatic)

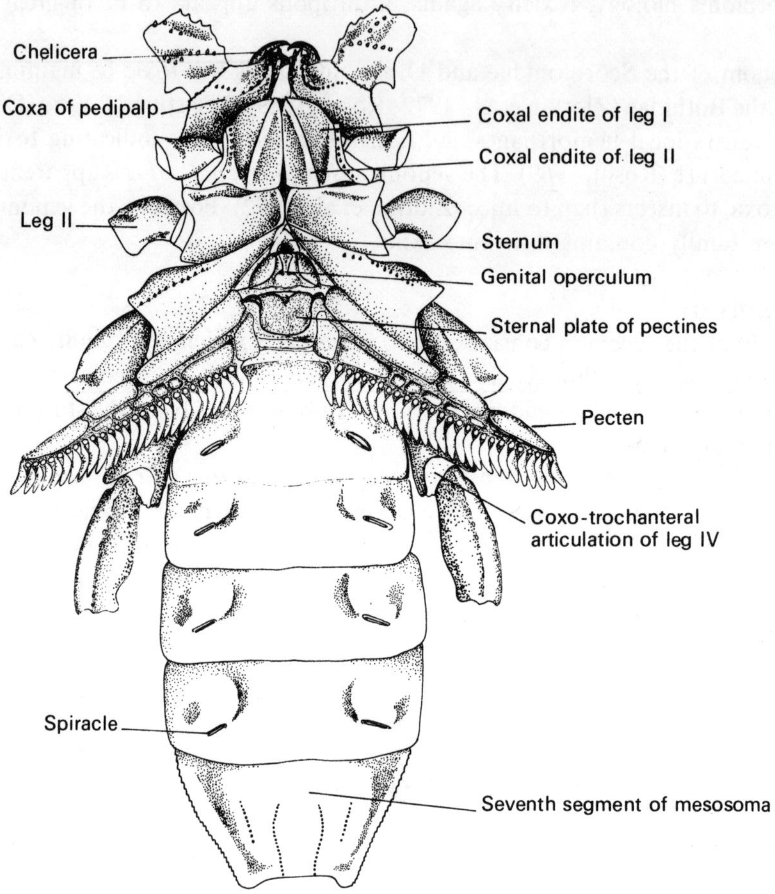

Fig. 2: Ventral view of prosoma and mesosoma (diagrammatic)

four pairs of legs. Each chelicera is three-segmented; the terminal segment is a movable finger, opposed to a similar fixed process of the second segment. The teeth of the chelicerae are characteristic for families and sometimes also for genera (Figs. 3–6). The pedipalp (Fig. 7) consists of six segments, the distal article forming a movable finger opposing an immovable finger of the fifth segment. Of great specific importance are the form of the crests, the granulation and arrangement of the trichobothria on the pedipalps and the arrangement of the denticles on the cutting edge of the fingers of the pedipalp (Fig. 8). Each walking leg consists of seven segments, the last bearing two claws. Of systematic importance are spurs, bristle-combs and the arrangement of spines on the distal segments of the legs (Figs. 9–17).

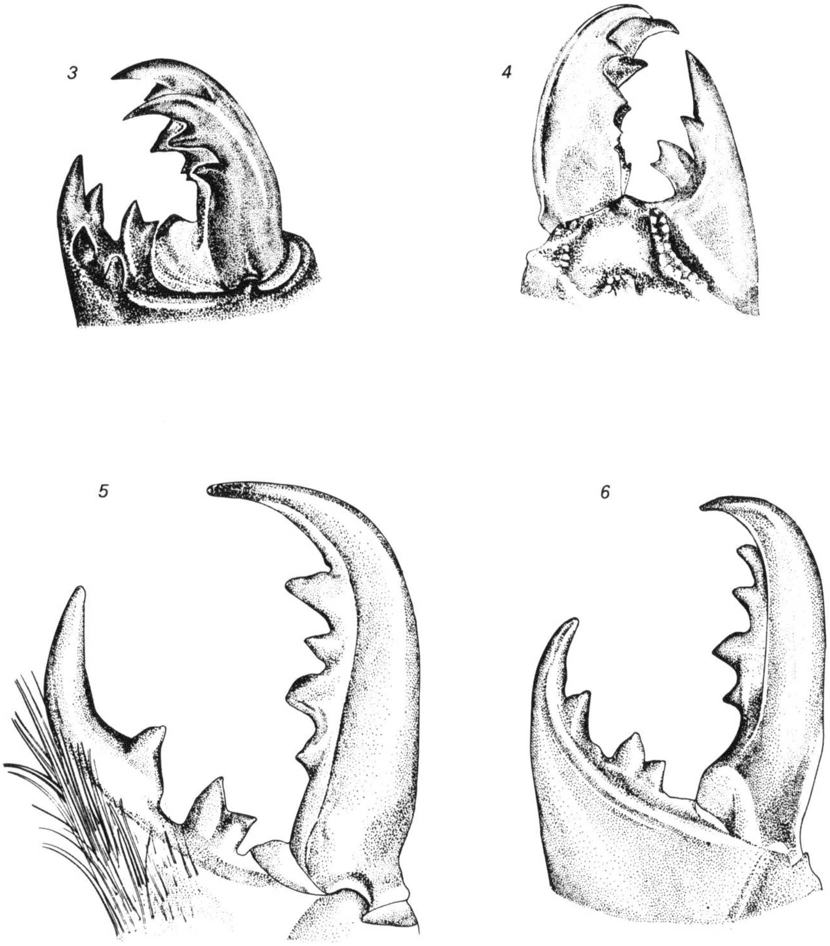

Figs. 3–6: Chelicerae
3. buthid, ventral; 4. buthid, dorsal; 5. *Scorpio*, ventral; 6. *Nebo*, ventral

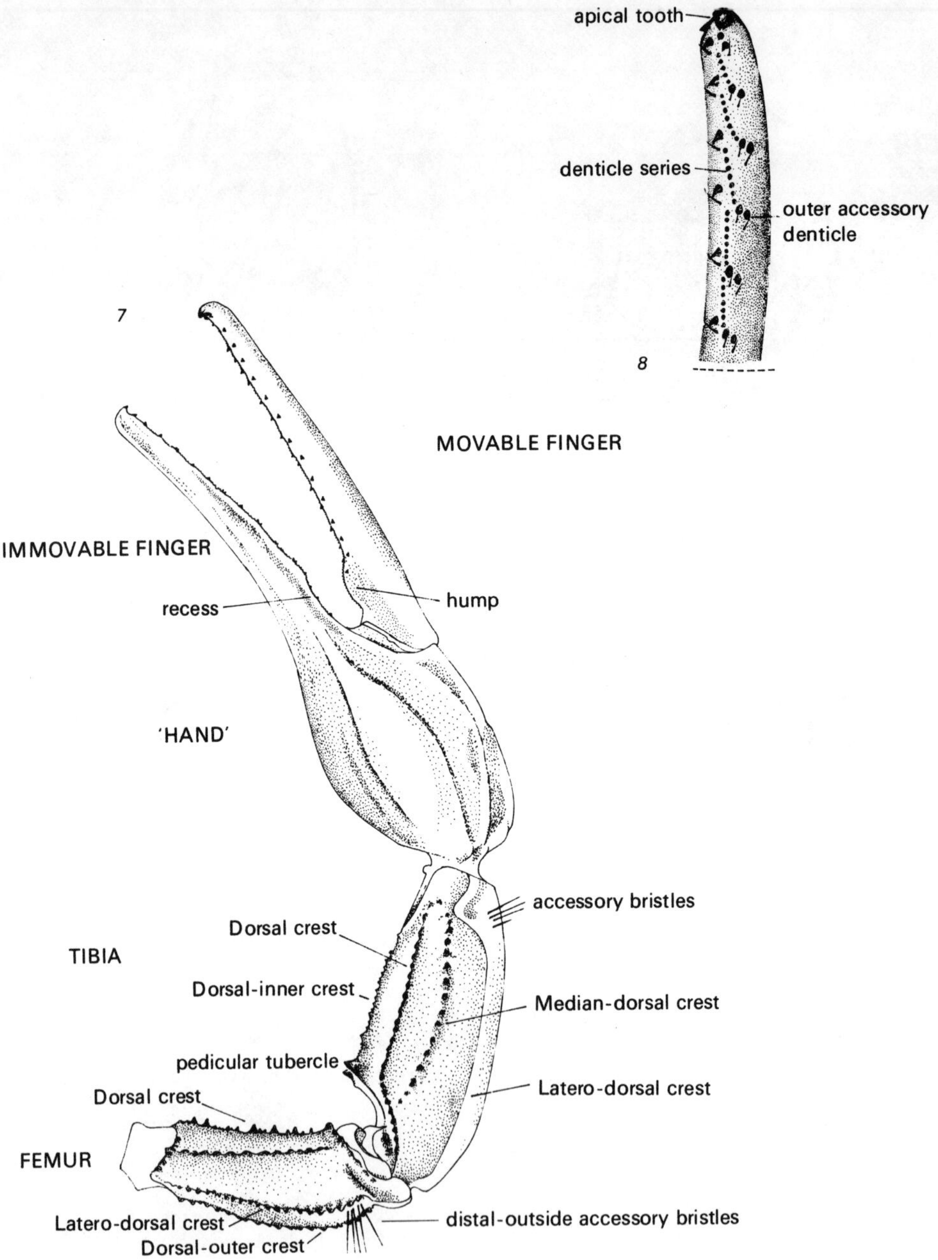

Figs. 7–8: Pedipalp
7. dorsal view (diagrammatic); 8. denticles on cutting edge of movable finger

9

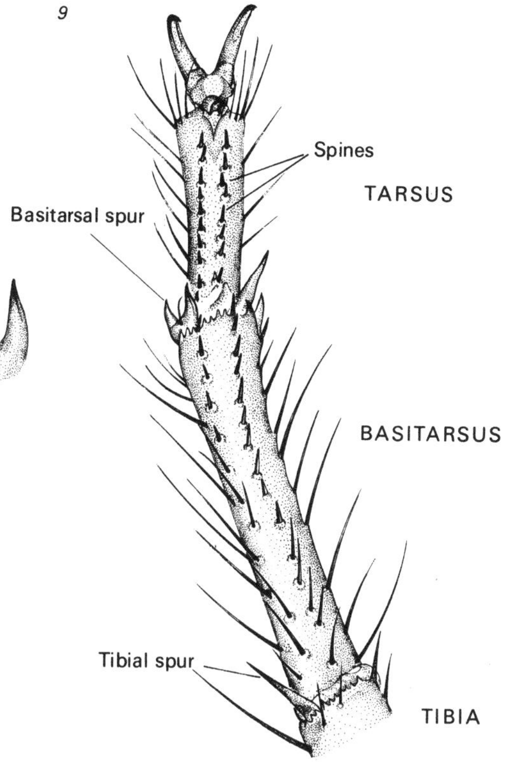

10

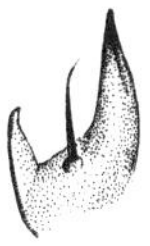

11

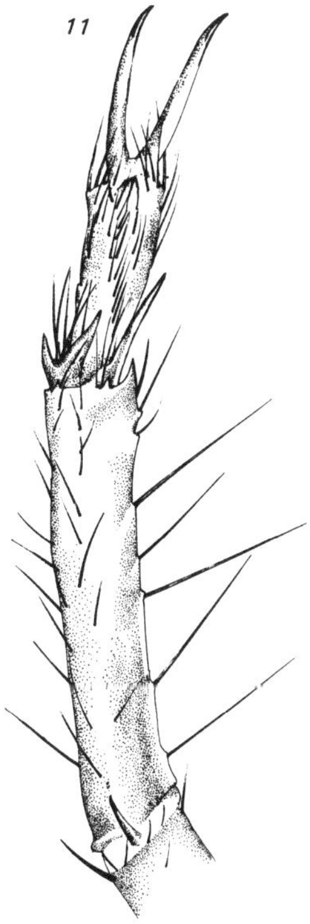

12

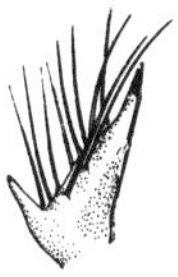

13

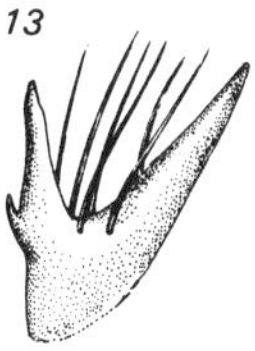

14

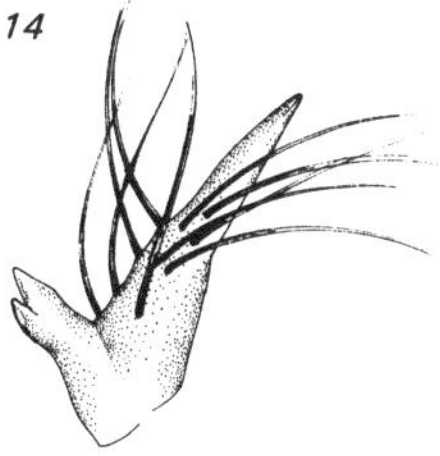

Figs. 9–10: *Buthotus judaicus*. 9. distal segments of walking leg bearing spines, ventral; 10. basitarsal spur (enlarged). Figs. 11–12: *Buthacus leptochelys*. 11. distal segments of walking leg bearing bristles, ventral; 12. basitarsal spur (enlarged). Figs. 13–14: Basitarsal spur (enlarged). 13. with basal bifurcation (*Androctonus bicolor*); 14. with distal bifurcation (*A. australis*)

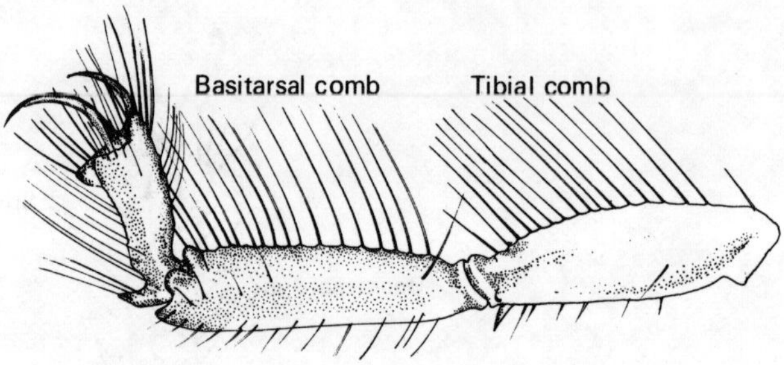

Fig. 15: Distal segments of walking leg with tibial and basitarsal combs of bristles, lateral (*Buthacus leptochelys*)

16

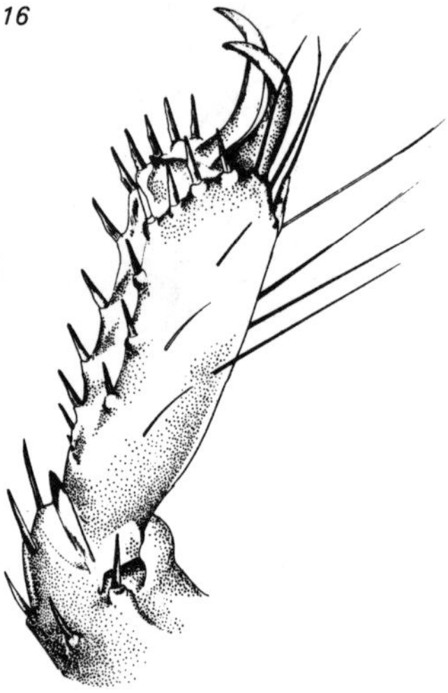

17

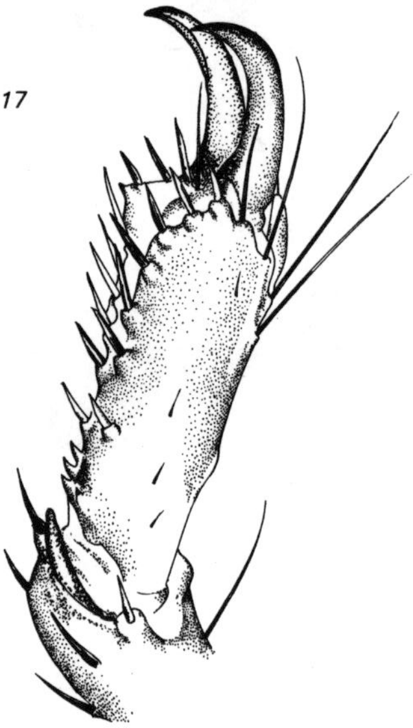

Figs. 16–17: Tarsus, lateral. 16. *Scorpio maurus*; 17. *Nebo*

Families are distinguished by the form of the *sternum* (Figs. 18–19).

18

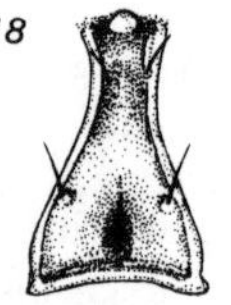

19

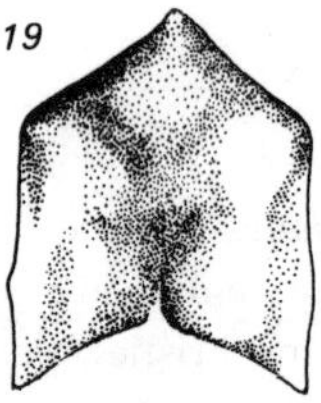

Figs. 18–19: Sternum (diagrammatic). 18. Buthidae; 19. Scorpionidae and Diplocentridae

Each of the seven segments of the mesosoma bears 1–5 dorsal crests (Fig. 1). The first sternite is markedly reduced and bears the genital opening covered by the genital opercula (Fig. 2). These are frequently fused in the middle in females and completely or partly separated in males. Males may usually be recognized by the presence of two genital papillae under the genital opercula. The second segment bears a small rectangular sternal plate (Fig. 2) to which comb-like appendages, the *pectines*, are attached. Each pecten (Figs. 20–21) usually consists of an anterior marginal lamella, middle lamellae, a row of triangular fulcra and denticles. A pair of spiracles (Fig. 2) is present on the lateral part of sternites 3–6. The spiracles are the opening of lamellate tracheae known as book lungs.

The metasoma (Figs. 22–23) consists of five cylindrical segments and the stinger. Surface structures like the dorsal groove, the different development of crests, granulation, depressions and pilosity are of systematic importance. The *stinger* (Fig. 24) consists of a large bulbous vesicule and a long, curved aculeus. The venom glands open at the end of the stinger. A subaculear tubercle is present in some species (Fig. 24).

20

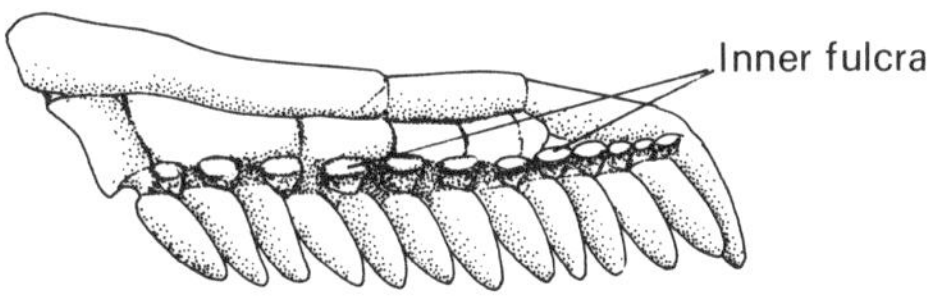

21

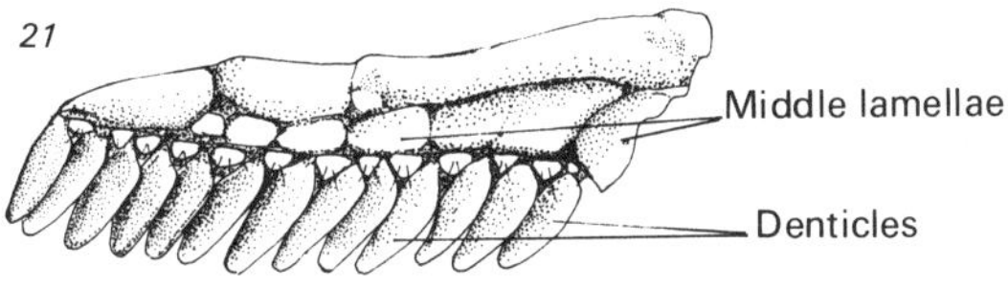

Figs. 20–21: Pecten of a buthid (diagrammatic). 20. outer view; 21. inner view

Key to the Families of Scorpions in Israel and Sinai

1.	Sternum triangular (Fig. 18).	**Buthidae,** p. 13
–	Sternum pentagonal (Fig. 19)	2
2.	Stinger without subaculear tubercle.	**Scorpionidae,** p. 102
–	Stinger with large subaculear tubercle (Fig. 24).	**Diplocentridae,** p. 115

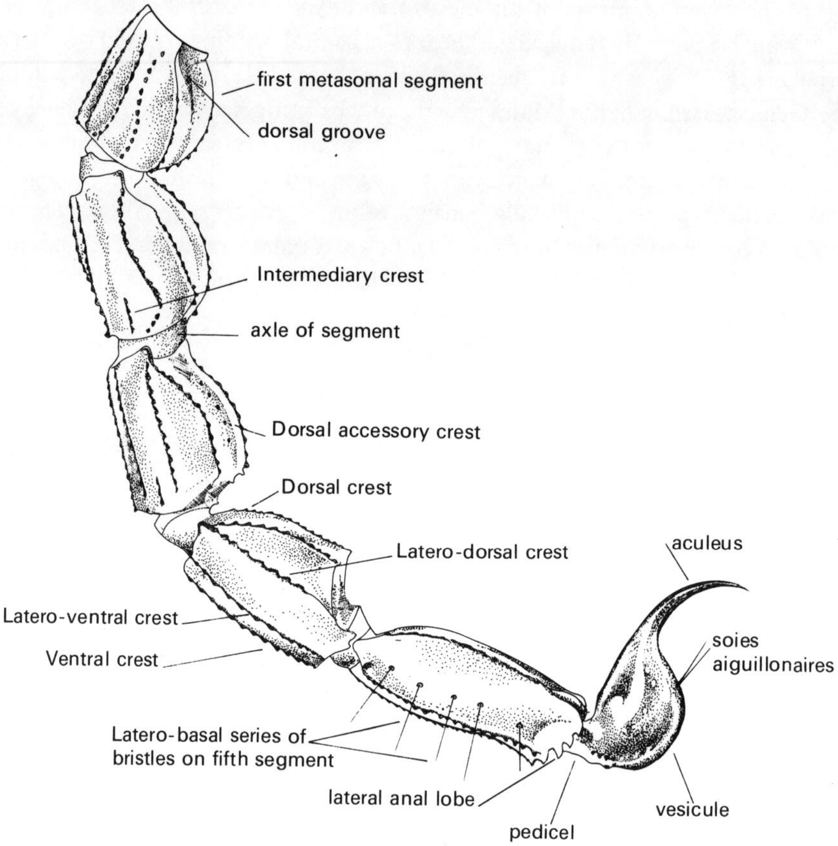

Fig. 22: Metasoma and stinger, lateral (diagrammatic)

23

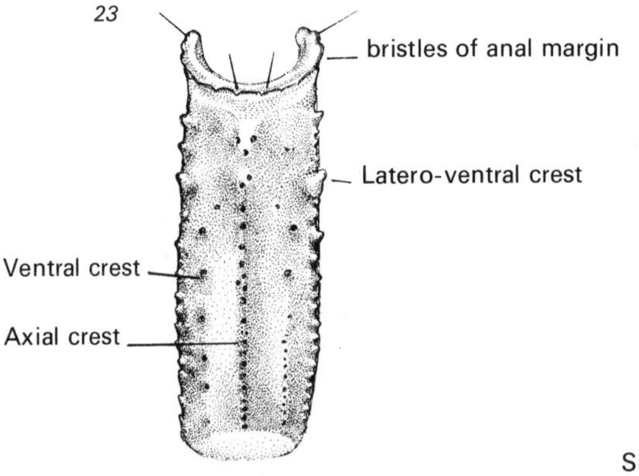

24

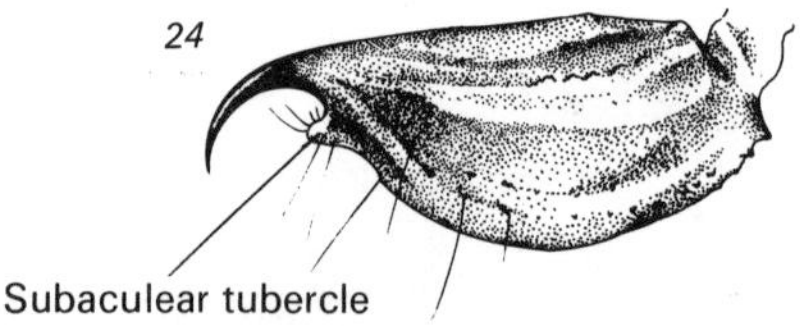

Fig. 23: Fifth segment of metasoma, ventral (diagrammatic)
Fig. 24: Stinger of *Nebo*

Family BUTHIDAE Simon, 1879

Les Arachnides de France, Paris, 7:92

Type Genus: *Buthus* Leach, 1815.

Diagnosis: Sternum triangular; middle lamellae of pectines elongate, never round or bead-like; three to five lateral eyes.

The Buthidae are the largest family of scorpions. Kraepelin (1899) divided the family into two subfamilies: Centrurinae, distributed mainly in the New World, and Buthinae, occurring mainly in the Old World. Later (1905), he distinguished four subfamilies, of which only the Buthinae occur in our region. Vachon (1973) lists 42 genera in the Buthidae, of which seven are represented in Israel.

Subfamily BUTHINAE Kraepelin, 1899

Das Tierreich, 8. Lief., Berlin: 6

Diagnosis: Movable finger of pedipalps without broadly overlapping series of denticles and without accompanying lateral series of denticles.

There are numerous genera in this subfamily; the systematic position of some genera and subgenera is still under discussion. The following genera are represented in our region: *Buthus* Leach, 1815; *Androctonus* Hemprich & Ehrenberg, 1829; *Leiurus* Hemprich & Ehrenberg, 1829; *Orthochirus* Karsch, 1891; *Buthacus* Birula, 1908; *Compsobuthus* Vachon, 1949; *Buthotus* Vachon, 1949.

Since the genus *Buthus* was established, about a hundred species and many subspecies, distributed throughout Africa and Asia, have been described. This large number of often very different 'forms' obviously necessitated the division of the genus into smaller, more homogeneous groups.

The outlines of such grouping were given by Kraepelin (1891). However, Kraepelin placed only six 'species' in the genus *Buthus* and considered all the others as synonyms of these species. Each of Kraepelin's 'species' is at present considered a genus: *B. leptochelys* = *Buthacus*; *B. hottentotta* = *Buthotus*; *B. doria* = *Odontobuthus* Vachon, 1950; *B. gibbosus* = *Mesobuthus* Vachon, 1950; *B. quinquestriatus* = *Leiurus*; *B. occitanus* = *Buthus*. Kraepelin (1891, 1895) still considered *Androctonus* as a separate genus from *Buthus*.

Pocock (1895) criticized the work of Kraepelin (1891), and Kraepelin himself (1895) also made many changes. Still later, however (1899), he abandoned his classification. He even came to consider the genus *Androctonus* as a synonym of *Buthus*. However, Pocock, Birula, Werner and Pallary retained some of Kraepelin's groups. Birula (1908) isolated the group of *B. leptochelys* as the genus *Buthacus*. *Hottentotta*, *Prionurus* (including *Androctonus*) and *Buthus* were considered subgenera.

Vachon's comprehensive work on the North African species of scorpions (1948–1951) included a revision of the genus *Buthus*. He defined eight groups and established them as genera. *Buthacus* and the old genus *Androctonus* were reinstated. The subgenera *Leiurus* and *Hottentotta* (as *Buthotus* Vachon, 1949) were raised to genera. Three new genera were established: *Compsobuthus, Mesobuthus* and *Odontobuthus*. *Buthus* was left with only a few species.

Key to the Genera of Buthidae in Israel and Sinai

1. Anterior tergites of mesosoma with five crests. **Leiurus** Hemprich & Ehrenberg
– Anterior tergites of mesosoma without or with indistinct crests, or with only three crests 2

2. Tergal crests of mesosoma distinct 3
– Tergal crests of mesosoma indistinct or absent 6

3. Tergal crests posteriorly attenuated and projecting beyond posterior margin of tergites; prosoma with median-central and median-posterior crests united and forming a straight continuous line (Fig. 58); sole of tarsi of walking legs with bristles or hairs. **Compsobuthus** Vachon
– Tergal crests not projecting beyond posterior margin of tergites 4

4. Prosoma with latero-central crests united posteriorly with median-posterior crests forming a lyra-shaped figure (Fig. 26). **Buthus** Leach
– Crests of prosoma not forming a lyra 5

5. Sole of tarsi of walking legs with spines (Fig. 9). **Buthotus** Vachon
– Sole of tarsi of walking legs with hairs or bristles. **Androctonus** Hemprich & Ehrenberg

6. Crests of prosoma usually absent or indistinct (Fig. 71); prosoma without depressions behind median eyes; segments of metasoma without small depressions. **Buthacus** Birula
– Prosoma without crests but with deep depressions behind median eyes (Fig. 87); posterior segments of metasoma with small depressions (Fig. 88). **Orthochirus** Karsch

Genus BUTHUS Leach, 1815

Trans. Linn. Soc. Lond., 11 : 391

Type Species: *Scorpio occitanus* Amoreux, 1789.

Diagnosis: Prosoma with latero-central crests united posteriorly with the median-posterior crests, forming a lyra-shaped figure; anterior tergites of mesosoma with only three crests; always three denticles under apical tooth of movable finger of pedipalp.

Prosoma: Granulate, with distinctly granulate crests; median-central crests isolated and forming an H-shaped figure; latero-posterior crests generally absent, occasionally concealed among adjacent granules; posterior margin of prosoma slightly concave in the middle; median eyes small, separated from each other by more than their diameter.

Mesosoma: Tergites at least partly granulate, with distinct crests at least from third segment onwards; crests of seventh sternite usually granulate, rarely smooth.
Metasoma: Slender, segments of the same width or slightly narrower distally; anterior segments concave dorsally, but concavity gradually decreasing posteriorly; intermediary crests present on second and third segments, rarely on the fourth; segments 1–4 with distinct, granulate dorsal crests; latero-ventral crests of fifth segment usually with irregular granules; lateral anal lobes of fifth segment distinct; vesicule globular, without subaculear tubercle.
Pectines: Inner fulcra with a short sclerotized point.
Pedipalps: Crests of tibia distinct; hand smooth, rarely with crests; fingers with one outer accessory denticle near each series of denticles.
Walking Legs: Outer tooth of basitarsal spur simple and with a varying number of bristles; basitarsi of three anterior legs with a comb of bristles dorsally; sole of tarsi with long bristles or hairs.

Review of Genus: According to Vachon (1949), there are only three species in *Buthus*. *Buthus atlantis* Pocock, 1889 and *B. maroccanus* Birula, 1903b are known from Morocco. *Buthus occitanus* has a wide distribution: southern Europe, the whole of northern Africa to Sinai and Israel. *Buthus occitanus* forms numerous local 'forms' with a considerable variation of characters.

Buthus occitanus (Amoreux, 1789)

Scorpio occitanus Amoreux, 1789, *J. Physique*, Paris, 35 : 9–15. Type Locality: district of Languedoc, southern France.
Buthus occitanus —. Kraepelin, 1891, *Jb. Hamb. Wiss. Anst.*, 8 : 54 (in part); Vachon, 1949, *Archs Inst. Pasteur Algér.*, 27 : 155–160.

Coloration: Light yellow to dark brown, occasionally with dark bands on mesosoma, and dark fifth segment of metasoma and stinger.
Prosoma: Crests distinct: latero-posterior crests present but often concealed among adjacent granules.
Metasoma: Aculeus of varying length but usually not longer than vesicule including pedicel.
Pectines: Females with 19–30 denticles, males with 25–36 denticles.
Systematic Remarks: *Buthus occitanus* is widely distributed. It has been recorded from southern France, Spain and Portugal (Werner, 1902), Sicily (Simon, 1910; Werner, 1934), Malta (Werner, 1936) and Cyprus (Kraepelin, 1891) and the whole of northern Africa south to the Sahara, from Senegal to Somalia and Ethiopia. Hemprich & Ehrenberg (1829) described *Androctonus (Leiurus) tunetanus intermedius* from the coasts of Yemen (Lohaie). Kraepelin (1899) and Tullgren (1909), perhaps after Hemprich & Ehrenberg, recorded it from Arabia. However, this record was not confirmed in an examination of the large collection from Arabia and Yemen in the British Museum. Kraepelin (1891) recorded it from Israel (Jaffa) and Sinai. Its occurrence in Israel was further established by Shulov & Amitai (1959); specimens from Sinai have also been collected.

Vachon (1949) distinguished five subspecies of *B. occitanus* in North Africa: *B. o. occitanus, B. o. tunetanus, B. o. mardochei, B. o. malhommei* and *B. o. paris*. He further distinguished two variations of the first two subspecies and four variations of *B. o. mardochei*. Since then new material with further variations (Hoggar, southern Algeria; Agdz, Morocco) has been found. Birula (1909) described another subspecies, *B. o. barcaeus,* from Cyrenaica in Libya. Two other subspecies, *B. o. berberensis* and *B. o. zeylensis*, were described by Pocock (1900b) from Somalia. However, examination of Pocock's types and of additional material from Somalia showed that these two Somalian forms are in fact the two sexes of the same subspecies, the first the male, the second the female.

Shulov & Amitai (1959) described *B. o. mardochei* var. *israelis*. Examination of numerous specimens showed that the subspecies inhabiting southern Israel and Sinai is not the same as the Moroccan *B. o. mardochei. Buthus occitanus* may be vigorously forming subspecies. This is confirmed by comparison with specimens from Lower Egypt.

Buthus occitanus israelis (Shulov & Amitai, 1959)

Figs. 25–29; Map 1

Buthus occitanus mardochei var. *israelis* Shulov & Amitai, 1959, *Archs Inst. Pasteur Algér.*, 37(1): 218–225. Type Locality: Mash'abbe Sade, Israel; type lost.

Coloration: Light yellow; crests of prosoma and mesosoma sometimes slightly darker. *Size*: Medium-sized, 5–7 cm long.

Prosoma: Granulate, also between median-ocular crests, granulation densest laterally; crests very distinct in both sexes.

Mesosoma: Tergites granulate, mainly laterally; three crests very distinct, often beginning (mainly in males) from second tergite; four crests of seventh sternite granulate in females, almost smooth in males.

Metasoma: First segment distinctly wider than long or high in both sexes; second segment longer than wide in males, as long as wide or slightly wider than long in females; third segment slightly longer than wide in both sexes; fourth segment usually 1.3 times longer than wide in both sexes (1.2–1.5 times in males, 1.2–1.4 times in females); intermediary crests of segments 2 and 3 extending beyond half of segment; fourth segment without intermediary crests, rarely with 2–3 small, indistinct granules in males; ventral crests of segments 2 and 3 consisting of slightly crescent-shaped teeth which are more projecting in females; teeth increasing in size posteriorly, variable in number and irregularly spaced, occasionally with small denticles between the larger teeth; dorsal crests of fifth segment granulate almost throughout; lateroventral crests of fifth segment with irregular teeth; 2–4 smaller teeth between large subdistal and distal teeth, one of them, sometimes in both sexes, rather large; axial crest of fifth segment very distinct, bifurcate distally; fifth segment with two lateral anal lobes, occasionally with an additional small tooth on one side; segments 1–3 smooth, fourth segment sometimes slightly shagreened, fifth segment always com-

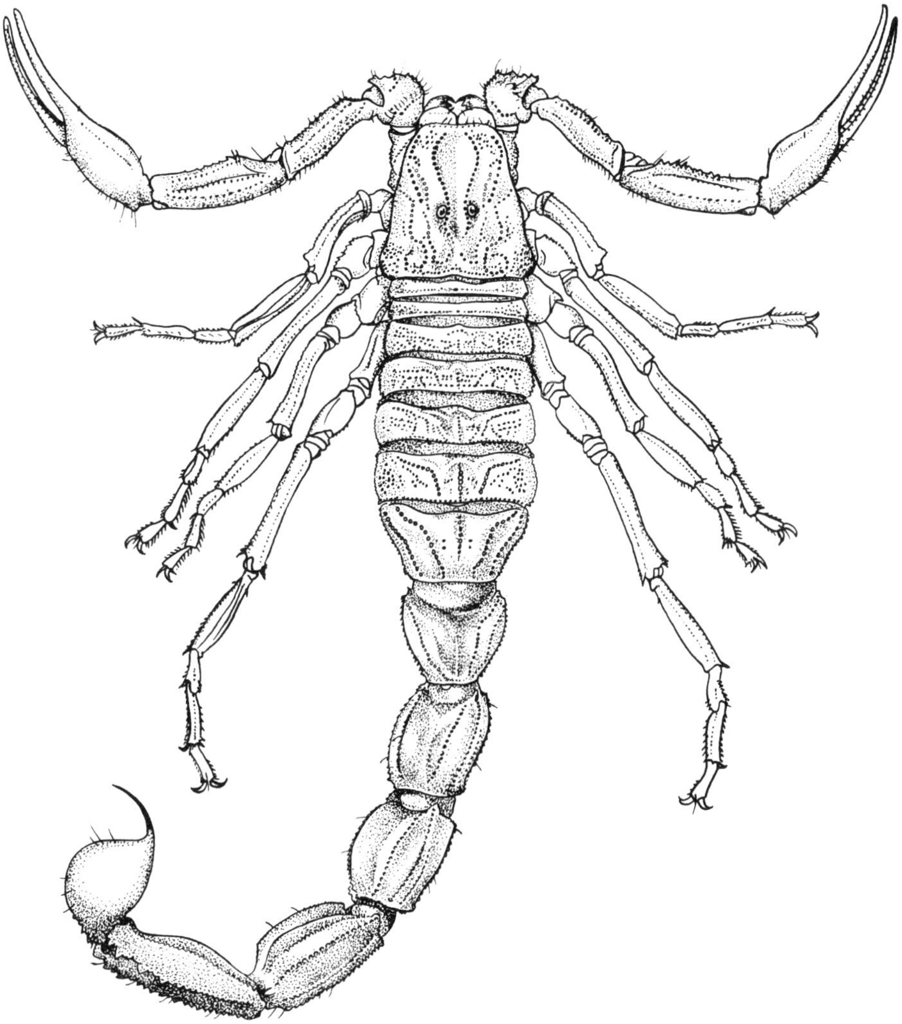

Fig. 25: *Buthus occitanus israelis* (Shulov & Amitai, 1959). Male from Yeroḫam, Israel (Sc. 1114); total length 57 mm

pletely shagreened; fifth segment with latero-basal row of more than four bristles (*'forme polytriche'* of Vachon), fourth segment also with a few bristles; vesicule slightly granulate ventrally; aculeus shorter than vesicule, without pedicel,* rarely of the same length, and shorter than width of vesicule.

Pectines: Extending in both sexes to or (mainly in males) beyond coxo-trochanteral articulation of leg IV; females with 22–28 (usually 25–26) denticles, males with 28–33 (usually 31–32) denticles.

Pedipalps: Femur smooth dorsally, with distinct crests, with accessory bristles on

* Measurement of length of vesicule, without pedicel in this species, from base of aculeus (= *'soies aiguillonnaires'* of Vachon, Fig. 22) to dorsal saddle of basal part of vesicule.

26

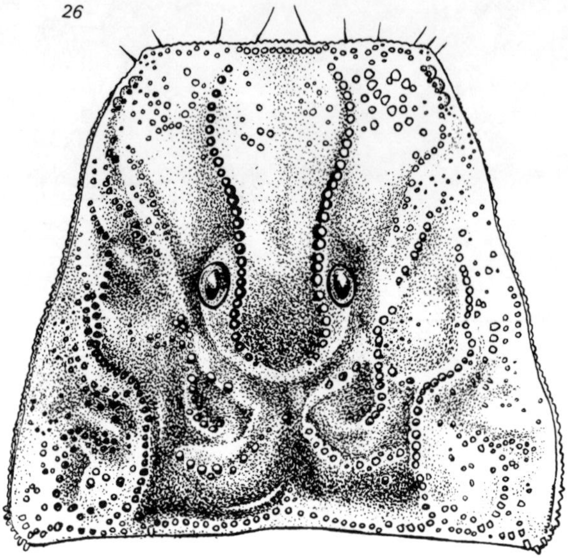

27

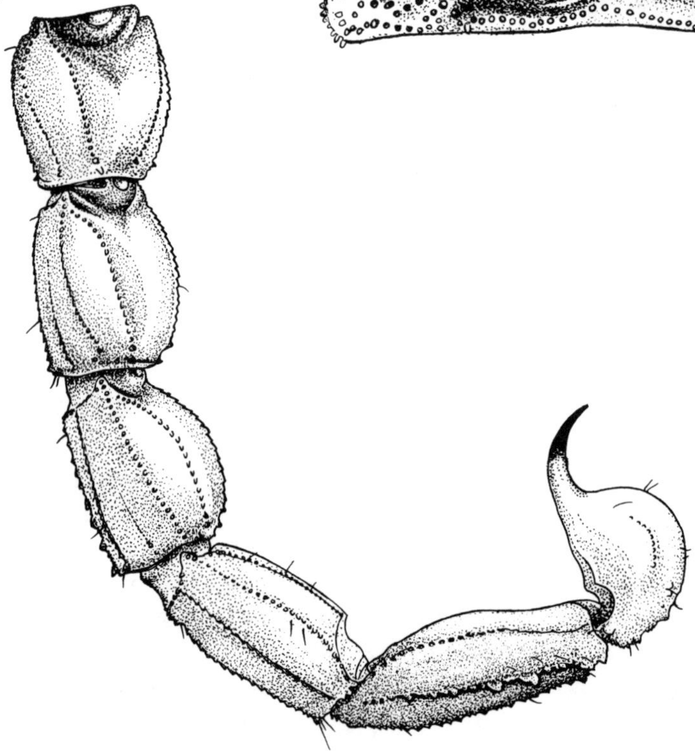

Figs. 26–27: *Buthus occitanus israelis* (Shulov & Amitai, 1959)
26. prosoma, length 5.9 mm; 27. metasoma, length 36 mm

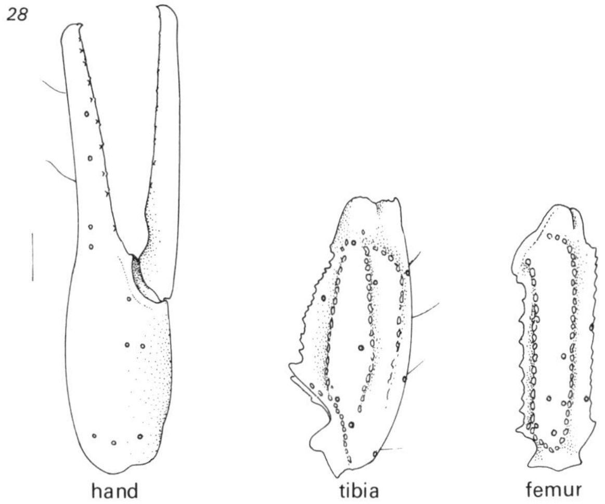

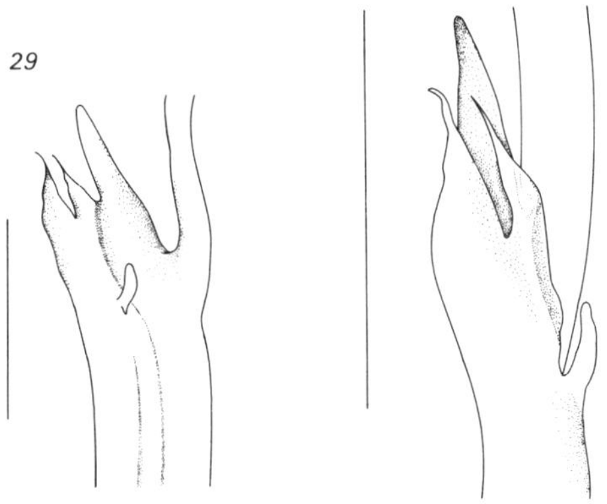

Figs. 28–29: *Buthus occitanus israelis* (Shulov & Amitai, 1959). 28. pedipalp, arrangement of trichobothria; 29: paraxial organ, form of lobes at base of flagellum; scale-lines 1 mm

outer side which are sometimes rather numerous; tibia smooth, with distinct, complete dorsal crests, with few (rarely numerous) accessory bristles on outer side; tibia of female wider than that of male, wider than femur in both sexes; hand smooth, with dorsal crest consisting of indistinct granules in male; hand wider in female than in male; hand of both sexes, but mainly of females, slightly wider than tibia; fingers longer than prosoma and distinctly longer than hand (1.7–2.1 times in males, 1.7–2.0 times in females); fingers of both sexes more than twice as long as width of hand; movable finger with 11–13 series of denticles.

Walking Legs: Anterior margin of coxae with granulate crests; basitarsus of three anterior legs with a comb of more than 10 bristles dorsally; outer tooth of basitarsal spur with 2–4 hairs; sole of tarsi with long and short bristles in two rows.

Measurements (mm): *Female*. Adult, Yeroḫam (No. Sc. 1120). Total length 62; prosoma 6, mesosoma 20, metasoma 36. Segments of metasoma: first L3.5, W4.5,

H3.9; second 4.3–4.4–3.9; third 4.4–4.3–4.0; fourth 4.9–4.1–3.6; fifth 5.5–4.2–3.6. Vesicule (without pedicel) L3.2, W3.5; pedicel of vesicule L0.7, W1.8; aculeus L2.8. Pedipalps: femur L5.4, W1.8; tibia L6.2, W2.6; hand L3.6, W2.9; movable finger L6.9. Number of denticles of pectine 25–26.

Male: Adult, Yeroẖam (No. Sc. 555). Total length 59; prosoma 6, mesosoma 16, metasoma 37. Segments of metasoma: first L3.7, W4.5, H3.7; second 4.6–4.5–3.7; third 4.6–4.4–3.7; fourth 5.3–3.9–3.4; fifth 6.0–3.9–2.8. Vesicule (without pedicel) L3.2, W3.0; pedicel of vesicule L0.5, W1.6; aculeus L2.5. Pedipalps: femur L5.1, W1.6; tibia L5.9, W2.3; hand L3.2, W2.3; movable finger L6.6. Number of denticles of pectine 31–32.

Distribution, Israel and Sinai (Map 1): References of previous records from Israel

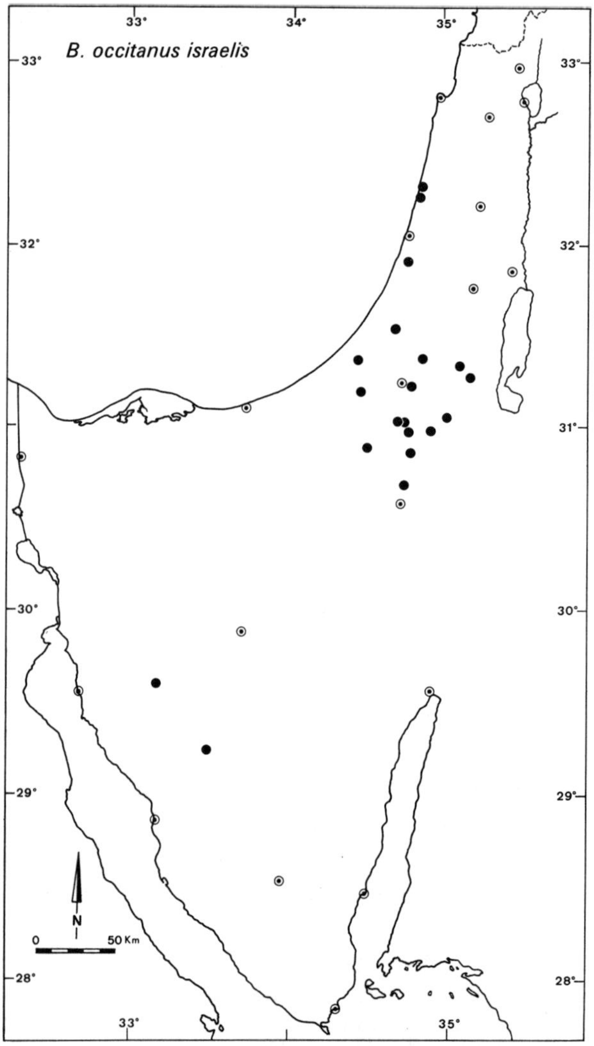

Map 1: Records of *Buthus* in Israel and Sinai

and Sinai are summarized in the Appendix on Distribution. *Buthus occitanus israelis* probably occurs in most parts of Sinai and southern Israel. In Israel it extends north to the southern foothills of Judea, and along the Coastal Plain to about 30 km north of Tel Aviv.

Ecological Notes: *Buthus occitanus* is fairly common and is occasionally found in abundance in a small area. It occurs in the coastal sand dunes, on loess and sandy soil and in the stony desert. It lives under stones and in empty burrows of Isopoda and others. Parturition usually in September–October; about a dozen young. It is preyed upon by *Latrodectus* spiders.

Systematic Remarks: Many young and adult specimens from southern Israel were compared with specimens from North Africa, Libya, Egypt, Sudan, Somalia and Ethiopia.

Some specimens of *Buthus* from our region resemble specimens of the Moroccan *B. o. mardochei.* However, this resemblance is also present between our scorpions and specimens from Sudan and Ethiopia. On the other hand, specimens from Cyprus, Tunisia, Libya and Somalia are different. Thus it does not seem reasonable to assume that specimens from Israel, Ethiopia and Morocco belong to the same form while the large areas between them are inhabited by other forms. *Buthus o. tunetanus* is larger and more hairy and also differs in the ratio between vesicule and aculeus. *Buthus o. barcaeus* differs in having intermediary crests on the fourth segment of the metasoma, and *B. o. berberensis* is a much smaller and broader form in which the crests on the tibia and hand of the pedipalps project distinctly.

The scorpions of Lower Egypt show great variation of some characters. Specimens from Alexandria and Ramleh resembled scorpions from Israel almost exactly; specimens from Cairo resembled the Tunisian form more closely.

Genus ANDROCTONUS Hemprich & Ehrenberg, 1829

Berolini ex officina Academica: 117

Androctonus—. Vachon, 1948, *Archs Inst. Pasteur Algér.*, 26(3): 288.

Type Species: *Scorpio australis* Linnaeus, 1758; subsequent designation by Vachon, 1948.

Diagnosis: Metasoma thick, deeply concave dorsally and dorsal crests of segments 1–4 strongly raised posteriorly.

Prosoma: Granulate, with distinct granulate crests; median-central crests usually not united posteriorly with median-posterior crests and not situated exactly behind each other; latero-central crests separated from median-posterior crests; latero-posterior crests absent; posterior margin of prosoma almost straight; median eyes small, separated from each other by more than their diameter.

Mesosoma: Tergites at least partly granulate, with three crests which begin at least from third segment; crests of seventh sternite smooth or granulate.

Metasoma: Intermediary crests only on second and third segment; latero-ventral crests of fifth segment irregularly granulate; lateral anal lobes of fifth segment distinct; vesicule of stinger relatively narrow, rugose ventrally, without subaculear tubercle.
Pectines: Inner fulcra with one or several hairs or fine bristles.
Pedipalps: Crests of tibia distinct or indistinct; hand broad or slender; finger with one outer tooth in each series of denticles; always three denticles under apical tooth of movable finger; recess and hump of varying size, present or absent at base of finger.
Walking Legs: Outer tooth of basitarsal spur simple or bifurcate, with long bristles; basitarsus of three anterior legs with a comb of bristles dorsally; sole of tarsi with bristles or hairs.

Review of Genus: Hemprich & Ehrenberg (1829) included two subgenera, *Leiurus* and *Prionurus*, in *Androctonus*. *Leiurus* is now considered a genus, and *Prionurus* a synonym of *Androctonus*. Vachon (1948) stated that *Prionurus* is also preoccupied. Three species, *A. australis, A. amoreuxi* and *A. finitimus,* are mainly brightly coloured; the other five species are dark.
Androctonus has a wide distribution: India and Iran to the Mediterranean; Senegal to Sudan and Egypt in Africa. The status of some species is still highly problematic.

Androctonus australis (Linnaeus, 1758)	Throughout northern Africa, Sinai and Arabia
Androctonus crassicauda crassicauda (Olivier, 1807)	Caucasus, southern Turkey, Iran, Iraq, Syria, Israel, Jordan, Arabia
A. c. gonneti Vachon, 1948	Southern Morocco
Androctonus amoreuxi amoreuxi (Audouin, [1827])	Sahara, Sudan, Egypt, ? Arabia
A. a. baluchicus (Pocock, 1900)	Pakistan, Afghanistan
A. a. hebraeus (Werner, 1935)	Israel, Sinai
Androctonus bicolor bicolor Hemprich & Ehrenberg, 1829	Egypt, Sinai, Israel
A. b. aeneas (C. L. Koch, 1839)	Highlands of Tunisia and eastern Algeria
A. b. liouvillei (Pallary, 1924)	Morocco, Saharian slopes of Atlas
A. b. ssp.?	Tripoli
Androctonus finitimus (Pocock, 1897)	Western India
Androctonus mauretanicus mauretanicus (Pocock, 1902)	Morocco, western slopes of Atlas
A. m. bourdoni Vachon, 1948	Southern Morocco
Androctonus hoggarensis (Pallary, 1929)	Sahara
Androctonus sergenti Vachon, 1948	Morocco, Anti-Atlas

Key to the Species of Androctonus in Israel and Sinai

(Map 2)

1. Third segment of metasoma wider than long 2
– Third segment of metasoma longer than wide. **A. amoreuxi**
2. Hands of pedipalps broad and stout 3
Hands slender. **A. bicolor**
3. Teeth of latero-ventral crests of fifth segment of metasoma increasing in size posteriorly; dark species. **A. crassicauda**
– Teeth of latero-ventral crests of fifth segment of metasoma regular, hardly increasing in size posteriorly; coloration bright. **A. australis**

Androctonus crassicauda (Olivier, 1807)

Scorpio crassicauda Olivier, 1807, *Voyage dans l'Empire Othoman, l'Égypte et la Perse*, Paris, 3 : 96–97, pl. 42, fig. 2. Type Locality: Cachan, Iran.
Buthus crassicauda—. Simon, 1872, *Annls Soc. Ent. Fr.*, (5), 2 : 247.
Prionurus crassicauda—. Pocock, 1895, *J. Linn. Soc.* (*Zool.*) *Lond.*, 25 : 292, 307–309.
Buthus (Prionurus) australis crassicauda—. Birula, 1896, *Annu. Mus. Zool. Acad. Imp. Sci. St.-Pétersbourg*, 1 :232–238.
Buthus (*Prionurus*) *crassicauda*—. Birula, 1900, Moscou, *Izv. Lyub. Estestv.*, 98(3), No. 1:9.

Coloration: Light brown, reddish, greenish, or dark brown to black; pectines and end of pedipalps and legs light. *Size*: Sometimes over 10 cm long.
Prosoma: Coarsely granulate; median-ocular crests extending to anterior margin of prosoma or not; median eyes situated slightly anterior to middle; three lateral eyes distinct or concealed among adjacent granules, equidistant.
Mesosoma: Tergites granulate throughout; crests distinct from third segment, sometimes with 2–3 granules on first or second segments; anterior sternites smooth, mat or shining; sternite 7 smooth or granulate; sternites with only a few bristles.
Metasoma: With a deep concavity dorsally, also in the fifth segment; segments 1–4 with serrate or granulate dorsal crests ending in a large granule; dorsal groove of first segment smooth or granulate, other part smooth; spaces between dorsal and latero-dorsal crests smooth or with small granules; latero-dorsal crests serrate, granulate or with partly fused granules; intermediary crests present only on posterior part of segments, reduced to 3–5 granules on second segment, 1–3 granules on third segment; sides of segments smooth, densely granulate or with only a few small granules; segments smooth ventrally or with a few coarse or small granules; latero-ventral crests of fifth segment with large teeth posteriorly extending to anal margin or ending before it; fifth segment with 2–4 lateral anal lobes; aculeus longer or shorter than vesicule; segments of metasoma and stinger with only a few bristles.
Pectines: Inner fulcra with one fine hair; females with 23–28 denticles, males with 27–35 denticles.

Pedipalps: Femur dorsally with minute granules and with accessory bristles outside distally; tibia smooth dorsally, shagreened or with small granules, without accessory bristles; hand broad, wider than tibia, smooth, inner side shagreened or with small granules; fingers long, slightly curved, with or almost without recess and hump at the base; movable finger with 12–16 series of denticles.

Walking Legs: Outer tooth of basitarsal spur simple, rarely bifurcate on some legs.

Systematic Remarks: Comparison of *A. crassicauda* from Israel and Sinai with material from Iran (Cachan and other localities), Turkey, Iraq, Syria, Jordan and Arabia, of the Muséum National, Paris, and the British Museum, confirmed Birula's observations (1905, 1917) that they all belong to the same subspecies. After examining local scorpions and specimens from Iran, Birula (1900 a, 1917) detailed some special characteristics of the Iranian specimens: latero-ventral crests of fifth segment, with large, lobed, outward-directed teeth posteriorly, which do not extend continuously to the anal margin; latero-dorsal crests of fifth segment granulate throughout; sides of segments of metasoma coarsely and densely granulate, but this could not be confirmed.

According to Birula (1900 b, 1903 a), another subspecies, *Prionurus crassicauda orientalis,* occurs in eastern Iran. The differential characters are: granulation on dorsal groove of first segment of metasoma and teeth of latero-ventral crest continuing to anal margin of fifth segment of metasoma. These characters are sometimes also present in specimens from Israel, so that this subspecies is apparently not valid.

Vachon (1948) described a new subspecies, *A. c. gonneti,* from southern Morocco (Akka), and later (1953) from Mauritania (Fort Trinquet). This subspecies is larger (African scorpions are usually much larger than Asian specimens) and differs from *A. c. crassicauda* mainly in the ratio between aculeus and vesicule and in its granulation. Vachon (1953) also described, without naming it, a single male from Mauritania (Molomhar) which differs slightly from *A. c. gonneti.*

The occurrence of *A. crassicauda*, usually considered an Asian species, in Morocco and Mauritania is rather surprising. It seems justified to recall the old controversy about the differences between the two species, the dark, mainly Asian *A. crassicauda* and the light, mainly African *A. australis.* Except for the differences in colour, the two species are apparently more closely related than was assumed. This view is supported by examination of specimens from Arabia. Further information about the ecological niche and distribution of the two species, from southern Sinai and Arabia where they may occur together, would be necessary to confirm this.

Androctonus crassicauda crassicauda (Olivier, 1807)

Figs. 30–34; Map 2

Description based on specimens from Israel and Sinai.

Coloration: Light to dark brown, ventral side light brown, posterior margin of anterior sternites sometimes with a band or triangular yellow area; end of fingers and of walking legs light brown. *Size*: Females may be more than 10 cm long.

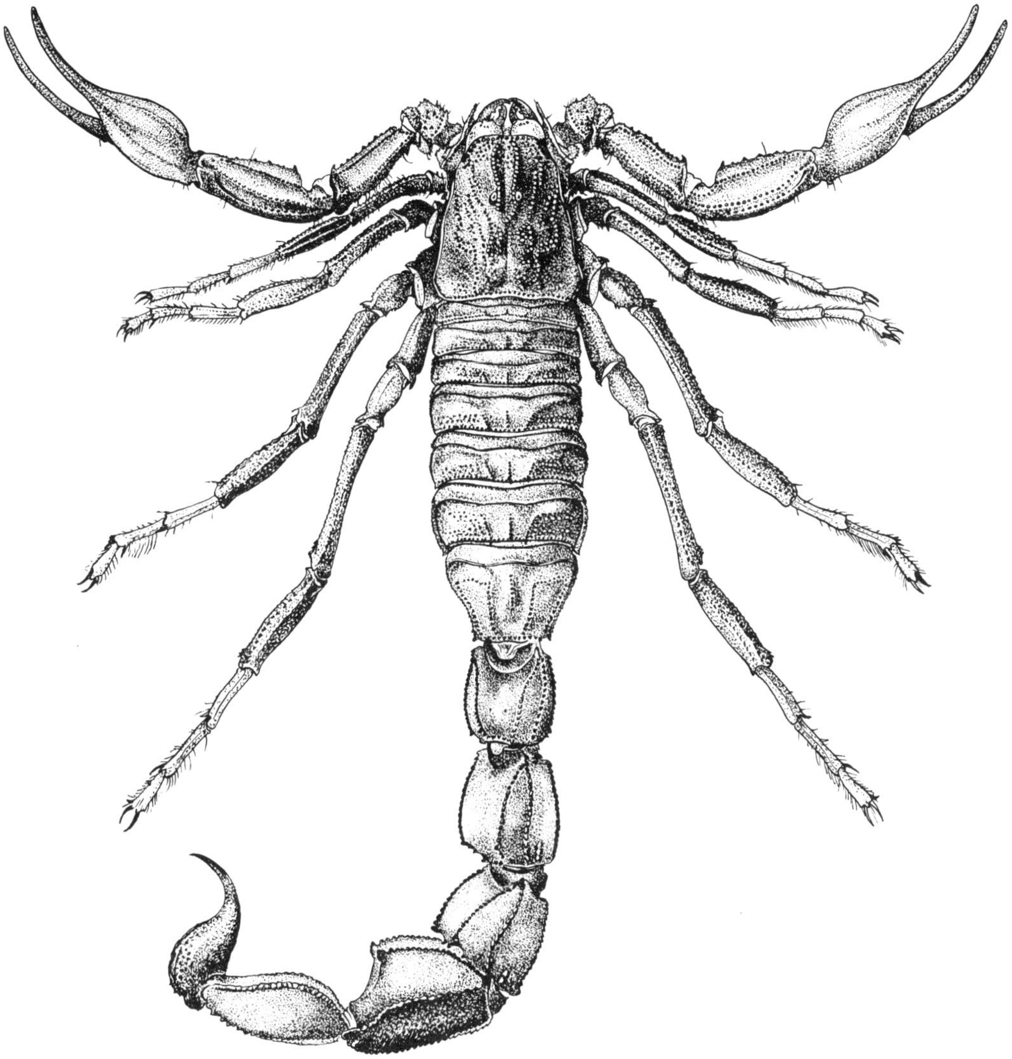

Fig. 30: *Androctonus crassicauda crassicauda* (Olivier, 1807). Male from Elot, Israel (Sc. 1291); total length 80 mm

Prosoma: Irregularly, not densely granulate; median-ocular crests not extending to anterior margin, granules of crests fused between median eyes, but separate behind eyes; median eyes of females separated from each other by more than twice their diameter, by twice or less than twice their diameter in males; three lateral eyes distinct, of about equal size.

Mesosoma: Tergites with irregular, coarse granulation mainly on posterior halves, posterior tergites sometimes almost without granules or only sparsely granulate; sixth sternite rarely with smooth, indistinct lateral crests; seventh sternite smooth, sometimes slightly shagreened laterally.

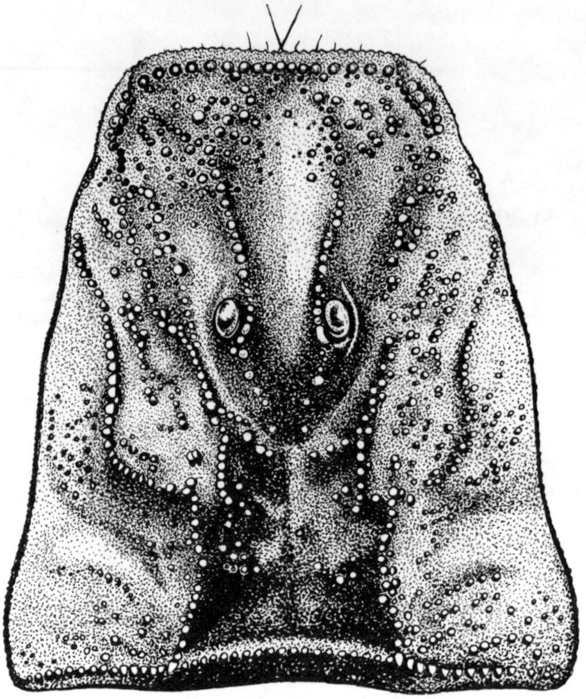

Fig. 31: *Androctonus crassicauda crassicauda* (Olivier, 1807). Prosoma, length 8.5 mm

Metasoma: Thick, widest on third segment; all segments wider than high; segments 1–4 wider than long; segments 3 and 4 wider than segment 1; fifth segment 1.3–1.4 times longer than high; dorsal groove and spaces between dorsal and latero-dorsal crests smooth, sometimes with a few small granules on first segment; latero-dorsal crests of segments 1–4 serrate or granulate, sometimes (mainly on segments 1–3 in males) with fused granules on anterior part of crests; crests of fourth segment in males and of fifth segment in both sexes in the form of raised lines without separate granules; sides of segments smooth or with a few small granules which increase in size slightly on the posterior segments; ventral crests of segments 1–4 with rounded, coarse granules or else smooth (mainly in males); first segment smooth ventrally or with a few small granules; segments 2–4 gradually more granulate with a few coarse granules; axial crests of fifth segment with large coarse granules throughout or with fused granules anteriorly; ventral crests with separate granules; anterior part of latero-ventral crests of fifth segment with small teeth in females and with fused granules in males, posterior part in both sexes with large blunt or sharp teeth continuing to anal margin; aculeus shorter than vesicule including pedicel but longer than width of vesicule; fifth segment 1.5–1.8 times wider than vesicule and 1.8–2.1 times wider than width of pedicel.

Pectines: In females extending to coxo-trochanteral articulation of leg IV, with 22–28 (usually 24–27) denticles; males with 27–34 (usually 29–31) denticles.

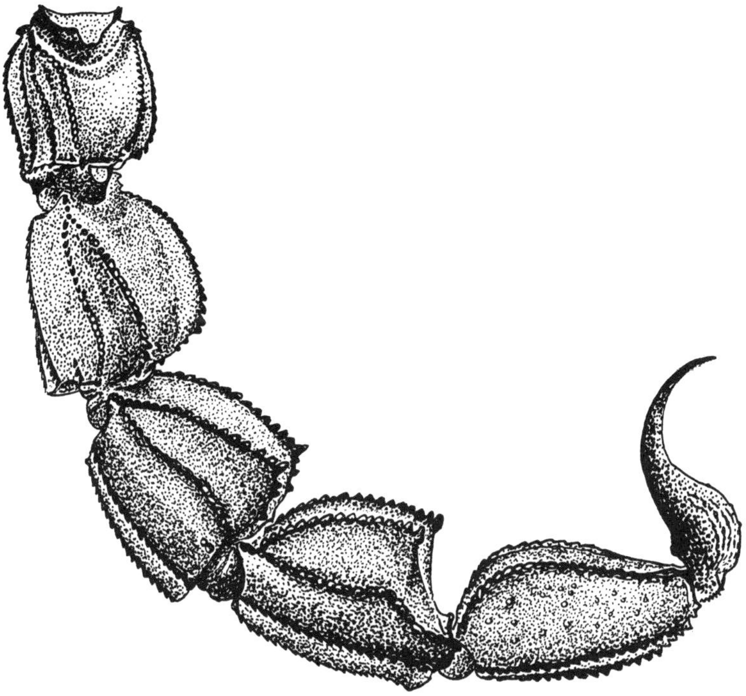

Fig. 32: *Androctonus crassicauda crassicauda* (Olivier, 1807)
Metasoma, length 48 mm

Pedipalps: Femur 2.5–3.0 longer than wide, sometimes with numerous accessory bristles; tibia 2.1–2.5 times longer than wide, its 'inner length'* about the same as its width; inner and dorsal-inner crests distinctly granulate; median-dorsal and latero-dorsal crests indistinct at their base, smooth or with fused granules; hand broad, 1.2–1.3 times longer than wide in both sexes and 1.3–1.7 times longer than 'inner length' of tibia; hand 1.1–1.2 times wider than tibia; recess and hump of varying size at base of finger; fingers longer than prosoma and about twice as long as hand; movable finger with 15 series of denticles.
Walking Legs: Outer tooth of basitarsal spur of leg IV with 6–15 bristles, tooth rarely bifurcate at base; dorsal comb of basitarsus of leg III with 12–17 bristles.
Measurements (mm): *Female.* Adult, Baqa el Gharbiya (No. Sc. 121). Total length 96; prosoma 11, mesosoma 31, metasoma 54. Segments of metasoma: first L5.8, W7.3, H6.0; second 6.8–7.5–6.7; third 7.0–7.9–7.3; fourth 7.5–7.7–7.0; fifth 8.0–7.0–5.6. Vesicule (including pedicel) L5.5, W4.1; pedicel of vesicule W3.6; aculeus L4.9. Pedipalps: femur L8.6, W3.0; tibia L10.2, W4.2; hand L6.6, W5.3; movable finger L12.5. Number of denticles of pectine 24–24.

* 'Inner length' of tibia = distance on inner side of tibia between pedicular tubercles and most proximal point of depression at base of articulation of tibia and hand.

33

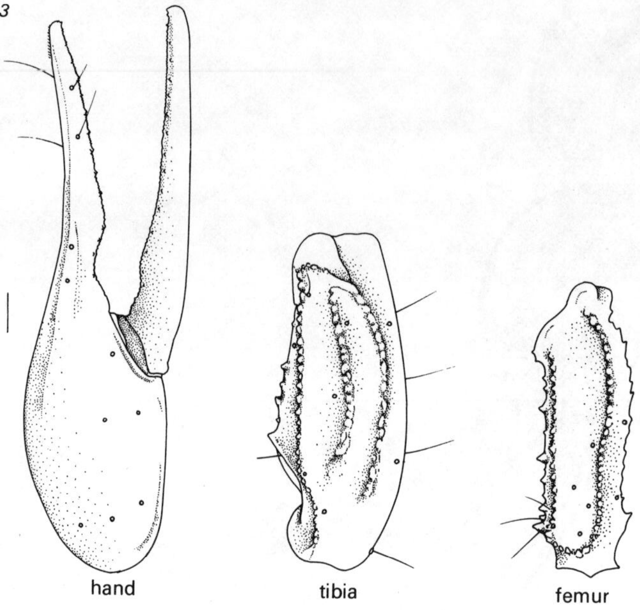

34

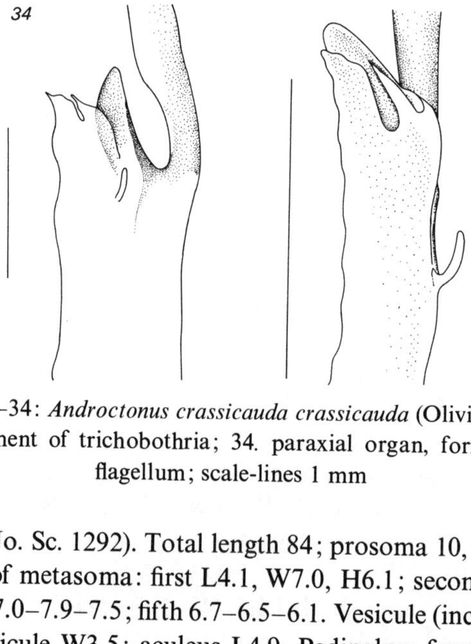

Figs. 33–34: *Androctonus crassicauda crassicauda* (Olivier, 1807)
33. pedipalp, arrangement of trichobothria; 34. paraxial organ, form of lobes at base of flagellum; scale-lines 1 mm

Male. Adult, Elot (No. Sc. 1292). Total length 84; prosoma 10, mesosoma 24, metasoma 50. Segments of metasoma: first L4.1, W7.0, H6.1; second 6.1–7.5–7.0; third 6.2–8.0–7.2; fourth 7.0–7.9–7.5; fifth 6.7–6.5–6.1. Vesicule (including pedicel) L5.1, W3.8; pedicel of vesicule W3.5; aculeus L4.9. Pedipalps: femur L7.7, W3.0; tibia L9.3, W4.4; hand L5.6, W5.0; movable finger L10.9. Number of denticles of pectine 30–30.

Distribution: The references of the following records are summarized in the Appendix on Distribution. Caucasus, Kurdistan, Turkey (southern Anatolia only), Iran,

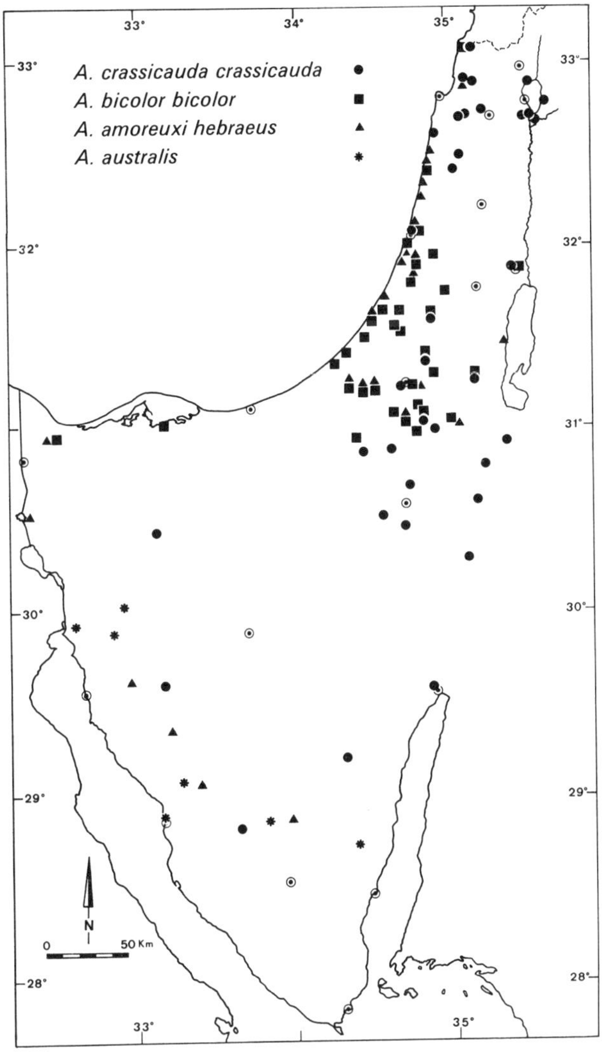

Map 2: Records of *Androctonus* in Israel and Sinai

Iraq (Mosul), Syria (Palmyra, Homs, Damascus), Jordan ('Arabia Petraea'; new records from the British Museum: Amman, Qasr Amra), Arabia (Muscat, Hadhramaut, Yemen).

Israel and Sinai (Map 2): *Androctonus crassicauda* is found almost throughout Israel and Sinai, but is probably absent in the sand dunes of northern Sinai and in a narrow zone along the southern Coastal Plain of Israel. No specimens of *A. crassicauda* have formerly been recorded from Sinai.

Ecological Notes: *Androctonus crassicauda* is not common. It is found mainly in mountainous areas on varying types of soil: terra rossa, basalt and rendzina to loess and sandy soils and stony desert. It lives under large stones and moves slowly.

Androctonus bicolor (Hemprich & Ehrenberg, 1829)

?*Scorpio australis* Herbst, 1800 (non Linnaeus, 1758). Audouin [1827], *Description de l'Égypte*, Paris, 22 : 412, pl. 8, fig. 3.
Androctonus (Prionurus) bicolor Hemprich & Ehrenberg, 1829, *Berolini ex officina Academica*: 123, pl. 2, fig. 4. Type Locality: coastal plain of Libya and Sinai mountains.
Androctonus aeneas C. L. Koch, 1839, *Die Arachniden*, Nürnberg, 6 : 3–6, pl. 181, fig. 432. Type Locality: North Africa.
Prionurus bicolor—. Pocock, 1895, *J. Linn. Soc. (Zool.) Lond.*, 25 : 307–309.
Buthus (Prionurus) australis bicolor—. Birula, 1896, *Annu. Mus. Zool. Acad. Imp. Sci. St.-Pétersbourg*, 1 : 236–238.
Buthus bicolor—. Kraepelin, 1899, *Das Tierreich*, 8. Lief., Berlin :17.
Buthus (Prionurus) bicolor—. Birula, 1908, *Sber. Akad. Wiss. Wien*, 117(2; 1):138–139.
Buthus (Prionurus) bicolor aeneas—. Birula, 1914, *Sber. Akad. Wiss. Wien*, 123(1) : 642–644.
Buthus (Prionurus) liouvillei Pallary, 1924, *Archs Inst. Pasteur Algér.*, 2(2) : 221, figs. 3–4. Type Locality: Morocco.
Prionurus bicolor longecarinatus Caporiacco, 1932, *Annali Mus. Civ. Stor. Nat. Genova*, 55 : 397. Type Locality: Libya.
Androctonus aeneas aeneas—. Vachon, 1948, *Archs Inst. Pasteur Algér.*, 26(3) : 297.
Androctonus aeneas liouvillei—. Vachon, 1948, *Archs Inst. Pasteur Algér.*, 26(3) : 299.
Androctonus bicolor aeneas—. Vachon, 1958, *Vidensk. Meddr. Dansk Naturh. Foren.*, 120: 125.
Androctonus bicolor liouvillei—. Vachon, 1958, *Vidensk. Meddr. Dansk Naturh. Foren.*, 120: 125.

Coloration: Dark to greenish brown or blackish olive, end of appendages light. *Size*: Larger than 9 cm.
Prosoma: Densely granulate; median-ocular crests usually not extending to anterior margin of prosoma, sometimes with slightly fused granules between median eyes; median eyes situated slightly anterior to middle.
Mesosoma: Tergites densely granulate; crests distinct from about first segment; crests of seventh sternite smooth, or only inner pair of crests smooth and lateral pair serrate or with fused granules; sternites with a few bristles.
Metasoma: Thick, third segment widest, with a deep concavity dorsally also on fifth segment; dorsal groove of first segment always granulate, other part smooth or sparsely granulate; intermediary crests of segments 2 and 3 of varying length and with a varying number of granules; latero-ventral crests of fifth segment with large teeth posteriorly; aculeus of varying length relative to length of vesicule; segments of metasoma and stinger with only a few bristles.
Pectines: Inner fulcra with one fine hair; females with 20–27 denticles, males with 26–32 denticles.
Pedipalps: Femur granulate and with accessory bristles outside distally; tibia with inner granulate or serrate crests, without accessory bristles; 'inner length' of tibia distinctly exceeding its width; hand wider or narrower than tibia; fingers long, slightly curved, with or without recess and hump at base; fingers more than twice as long as hand; movable finger with 13–16 series of denticles.
Walking Legs: Outer tooth of basitarsal spur simple or bifurcate.

Systematic Remarks: A young specimen of *A. bicolor* was collected by Hemprich & Ehrenberg (1829) in Beirut, Lebanon. This northernmost record was doubted by later authors. The species is, in fact, mainly found in southern Israel, but it ranges north along the Mediterranean coast as far as the northern border with Lebanon.

Hemprich & Ehrenberg indicated that Audouin's [1827] *Scorpio australis* may be *A. bicolor*, but the drawing given by Audouin is inaccurate in many details. However, the scorpion in Hemprich & Ehrenberg's drawing can be easily identified. Comparison of specimens from Israel and Sinai with material from Lower Egypt (Marsa Matruh, Ramleh, Abu Qir and Cairo) proves that our specimens belong to *A. bicolor bicolor*.

The above diagnosis of *A. bicolor* includes all subspecies. The North African subspecies may be a different species.

Birula (1914) stated that *A. aeneas* C. L. Koch is a subspecies of *A. bicolor*. Vachon (1948) disagreed and retained it as a separate species. He also considered *A. liouvillei* Pallary a subspecies of *A. aeneas*. Vachon (1958), however, accepted Birula's opinion and stated that both North African forms are subspecies of *A. bicolor*.

Androctonus bicolor aeneas from Algeria and Tunisia differs from *A. b. bicolor* in the short intermediary crests of the second and third segments of the metasoma (with only 2–5 granules in the posterior half of the segment).

Androctonus bicolor liouvillei differs from *A. b. bicolor* in the following characters: the hand of the male is wider than the tibia and as long as the 'inner length' of the tibia; a recess and hump are present at the base of the fingers; there are only a few granules in the short intermediary crests in the posterior part of the second and third segments of the metasoma. The Moroccan *A. b. liouvillei*, with its moderately thick hands, is apparently intermediate between *A. bicolor aeneas* and *A. crassicauda gonneti*, but the characters of *A. bicolor* are apparently predominant. The area of distribution of *A. b. liouvillei* lies between that of *A. b. aeneas* and *A. c. gonneti*. There are apparently one or two other subspecies in Libya. Caporiacco (1932, 1937) described *A. bicolor longecarinatus* from Ajedabya and Kufra, which he distinguished from *A. b. bicolor* of Egypt. Comparison of material from Tripoli showed that there is another subspecies which closely resembles *A. b. aeneas*, differing from it mainly in its very slender vesicule and in the very thin and long aculeus. This is probably the subspecies described as *A. aeneas* (Borelli, 1914, 1924, 1927; Schenkel, 1932; Caporiacco, 1937) but which actually inhabits Tunisia and Algeria.

Androctonus bicolor bicolor Hemprich & Ehrenberg, 1829

Figs. 35–38; Map 2

Coloration: Body dark to greenish brown, ventral side slightly lighter; hand, end of fingers and end of walking legs light brown. *Size*: Females may be over 9 cm long.

Prosoma: Densely granulate, with small granules and slightly larger granules anteriorly; median eyes in both sexes separated from each other by twice or less than twice their diameter; three lateral eyes distinct, all of the same size and equidistant.

Mesosoma: Tergites granulate, with small dense granules and slightly larger granules

Fig. 35: *Androctonus bicolor bicolor* Hemprich & Ehrenberg, 1829
Male from 'Arad, Israel (Sc. 1278); prosoma, length 6.7 mm

laterally; anterior sternites smooth, mat, third sternite slightly shagreened anteriorly, above the spiracles, sixth sternite sometimes with 2–4 smooth crests, seventh sternite smooth between median crests, slightly shagreened laterally.

Metasoma: Thick, all segments wider than high; segments 1–4 wider than long; segments 3 and 4 wider than segment 1; fifth segment 1.4–1.5 times longer than high; dorsal crests of segments 1–3 with large, rounded granules, granules on segment 4 sometimes slightly fused, crests ending with large granules on segments 2–4, sometimes also on segment 1; dorsal groove of first segment always with fine granulation which is sometimes dense on the bottom of the groove; dorsal groove of segments 2–5 smooth, shagreened or with only a few small granules; spaces between dorsal and latero-dorsal crests of segments 1–4 shagreened or with only a few small granules; granules of latero-dorsal crests of segments 1–3 large, rounded, or from second segment gradually fused posteriorly; latero-dorsal crests of fifth segment in the form of continuous raised lines; intermediary crests of second segment long, with 13–18 granules which are completely absent at the beginning of the segment; intermediary crests of third segment, with 6–17 granules, usually extending over three-quarters of length of segment, sometimes only granules in posterior half distinct; sides of segments with fine granulation which is slightly reduced on the fifth segment; ventral crests smooth or with fused granules, sometimes with separate granules on posterior segments; first segment almost smooth ventrally, slightly shagreened or with small granules, segments 2–4 gradually more granulate posteriorly, with a few coarse granules; axial crest of fifth segment with large, rounded granules which are sometimes

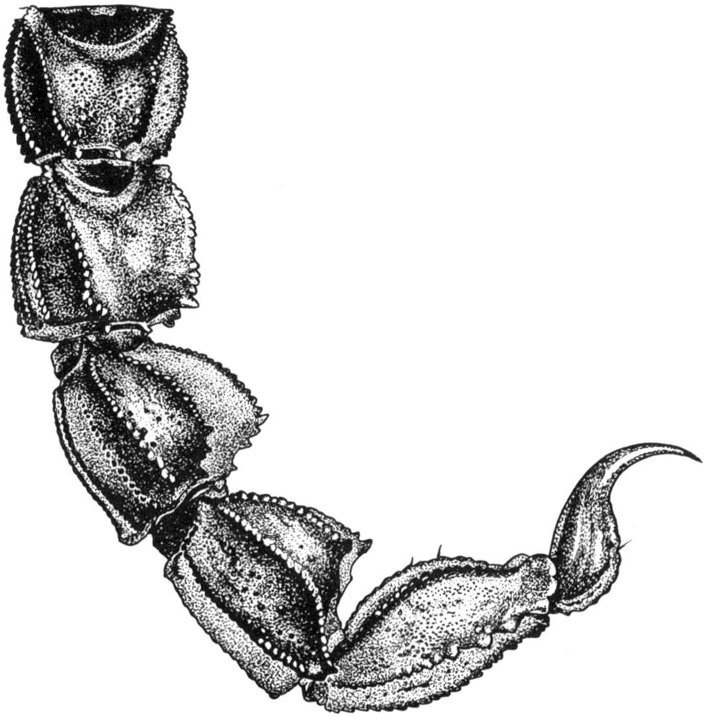

Fig. 36: *Androctonus bicolor bicolor* Hemprich & Ehrenberg, 1829
Metasoma, length 36 mm

slightly fused; ventral crests of fifth segment with spaced separate granules which are sometimes indistinct; latero-ventral crests of fifth segment with small, low teeth anteriorly, sometimes fused posteriorly, usually with large, lobed teeth, posterior teeth sometimes not very distinct, area to anal margin with smaller teeth; fifth segment with three distinct anal lobes; aculeus short or as long as vesicule including pedicel, rarely longer than vesicule; aculeus distinctly longer than width of vesicule; fifth segment 1.9–2.2 times wider than vesicule and 2.4–2.6 times wider than pedicel.
Pectines: In females barely extending to coxo-trochanteral articulation of leg IV, with 19–24 (usually 21–23) denticles; males with 23–29 (usually 26–28) denticles.
Pedipalps: Femur with fine granulation, 3.2–3.7 times longer than wide; tibia 2.8–3.4 times longer than wide, its 'inner length' 1.5–1.6 times greater than its width; dorsal inner crests with separate or fused granules, median-dorsal crests smooth or with separate or fused granules, latero-dorsal crests always smooth and indistinct at their base; hand very narrow in both sexes, 1.4–1.7 times longer than wide, distinctly shorter than 'inner length' of tibia and much narrower than tibia; hand smooth, only dorsal and inner side shagreened, sometimes marked slightly with smooth crests; fingers slender in both sexes, without recess and hump at their base; fingers longer than prosoma and about 3 times longer than hand; movable finger with 13–14 series of denticles.

37

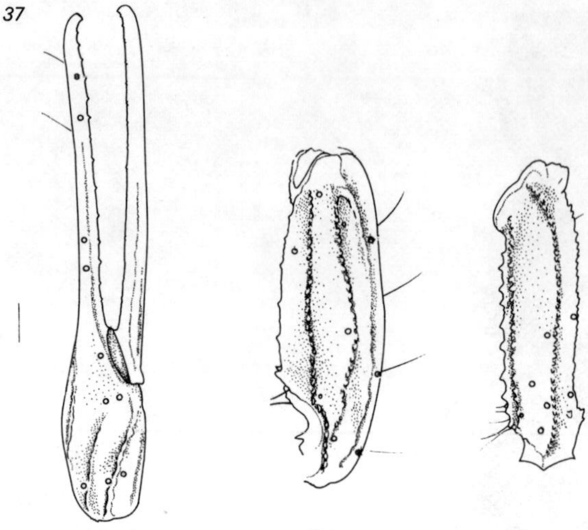

38

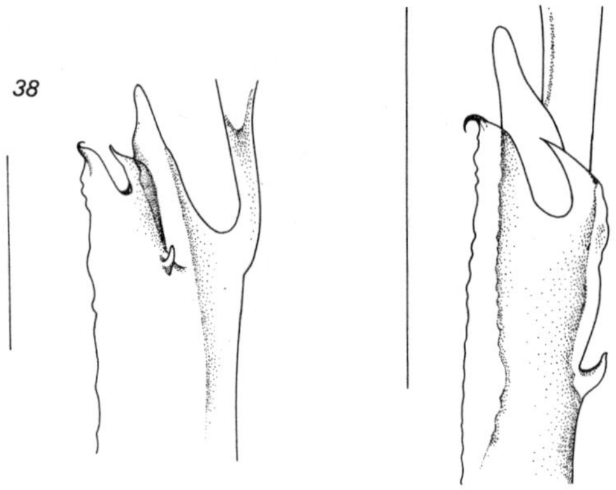

Figs. 37–38: *Androctonus bicolor bicolor* Hemprich & Ehrenberg, 1829
37. pedipalp, arrangement of trichobothria; 38. paraxial organ, form of lobes at base of flagellum; scale-lines 1 mm

Walking Legs: Outer tooth of basitarsal spur of leg IV with 5–10 bristles, tooth rarely bifurcate at base on some legs; dorsal comb of basitarsus of leg III with 12–18 bristles.

Measurements (*mm*): *Female*. Adult, Be'er Sheva' (No. Sc. 1544). Total length 85; prosoma 9, mesosoma 29, metasoma 47. Segments of metasoma: first L4.8, W7.4, H6.1; second 5.5–8.2–6.3; third 5.7–8.5–6.5; fourth 6.5–7.9–6.2; fifth 7.0–6.8–4.8. Vesicule (including pedicel) L4.7, W3.5; pedicel of vesicule W2.8; aculeus L4.6. Pedipalps: femur L7.4, W2.3; tibia L8.8, W3.1; hand L3.7, W2.5; movable finger L10.6. Number of denticles of pectine 22–24.

Male. Adult, Jericho (No. Sc. 718). Total length 72; prosoma 8, mesosoma 21, metasoma 43. Segments of metasoma: first L4.2, W6.4, H5.8; second 5.2–7.4–5.8; third 5.3–7.9–6.0; fourth 6.1–7.7–5.9; fifth 6.4–6.2–4.5. Vesicule (including pedicel) L4.4,

W2.8; pedicel of vesicule W2.4; aculeus L4.2. Pedipalps: femur L7.5, W2.1; tibia L8.5, W2.7; hand L3.4, W2.2; movable finger L9.7. Number of denticles of pectine 26–26.

Distribution: The systematic position of the different subspecies occurring in Libya is not clear. The references of the following records are summarized in the Appendix on Distribution. Egypt. ? Southeastern Eritrea: Pavesi (1885) mentions *A. aeneas* from Assab found in Graaf's Bouturlin collections; it is possibly *A. bicolor*.

Israel and Sinai (Map 2; p. 29): *Androctonus bicolor* occurs in a narrow zone from the north, along the whole Coastal Plain to Bir Gifgafa and Qantara in northern Sinai. In the northern Negev it extends to the foothills of Judea and to Jericho. It probably also occurs along the west and south shores of Sinai.

Ecological Notes: *Androctonus bicolor* is common mainly in the southern parts of Israel and the Jordan Plain, less common in the Mediterranean Coastal Plain. It is found in coastal and desert sand dunes, in brown-red sandy soils, brown steppe soils, loess-sandy and loess-like soils and in the stony desert. It lives under large stones; occasionally dozens of specimens are concentrated in a small stony area surrounded by terrain without stones. It sometimes inhabits burrows of rodents and small caves and empty cisterns. Parturition usually in August; number of young 30–40. It moves with agility and stings rapidly. It preys on small, usually soft-bodied arthropods.

Androctonus australis (Linnaeus, 1758)

Scorpio australis Linnaeus, 1758, *Systema Naturae*, 10th ed.: 624–625. Type Locality: Africa.

Androctonus (Prionurus) funestus Hemprich & Ehrenberg, 1829, *Berolini ex officina Academica*: 121, pl. 2, fig. 5. Type Locality: Dongala, Sudan.

Androctonus (Prionurus) libycus Hemprich & Ehrenberg, 1829, *Berolini ex officina Academica*: 121, pl. 2, fig. 1. Type Locality: coastal plain of Libya.

Androctonus (Prionurus) melanophysa Hemprich & Ehrenberg, 1829, *Berolini ex officina Academica*: 123, pl. 2, fig. 8. Type Locality: coastal plain of Libya and Sinai mountains.

Androctonus hector C.L. Koch, 1839, *Die Arachniden*, Nürnberg, 6: 6–8, pl. 181, fig. 433. Type Locality: North Africa.

Prionurus libycus—. Pocock, 1895, *J. Linn. Soc. (Zool.) Lond.*, 25: 306.

Buthus (Prionurus) australis—. Birula, 1900, Moscou, *Izv. Obshch. Lyub. Estestv.*, 98(3), No. 1: 8–9.

Buthus australis libycus—. Simon, 1910, *Bull. Soc. Ent. Égypte*: 64–65.

Androctonus australis—. Vachon, 1948, *Archs. Inst. Pasteur Algér.*, 26(4): 452.

Coloration: Body yellow; hand of pedipalp and posterior segments of metasoma yellow or black. *Size*: Sometimes more than 10 cm long.

Prosoma: Granulate, with small granules and with coarse granules anteriorly; median-ocular crests not extending to anterior margin of prosoma, granules of crests sometimes fused between median eyes but separate behind eyes; median eyes situated slightly anterior to middle and separated from each other by more than twice their diameter; three distinct lateral eyes.

Mesosoma: Tergites mainly with small granules in posterior half; crests distinct from third segment onward, sometimes from first or second segment; anterior sternites smooth, without crests; seventh sternite smooth or slightly shagreened laterally, inner pair of crests sometimes almost smooth or slightly granulate but less granulate than lateral crests; sternites with a few bristles.

Metasoma: Thick, third and fourth segments widest; segments 3–5 with very deep dorsal concavities; segments 1–3 wider than long; segments 4 and 5 of varying length; dorsal crests of segments 1–4 markedly projecting posteriorly with large granules, ending in a larger granule; dorsal groove and space between dorsal and latero-dorsal crests smooth, except first segment sometimes shagreened or with fine granulation; intermediary crests with only a few granules in posterior part of segments, at most extending to half the length of the second segment; sides of segments more or less smooth; ventral crests smooth, granulate or with fused granules mainly on anterior segments; segments smooth or with large granules ventrally, mainly on fourth segment; latero-dorsal crests of fifth segment granulate or in the form of raised lines with fused granules in anterior part of segment; axial and ventral crests regular, latero-ventral crests serrate or with coarse granules; fifth segment with three lateral anal lobes; aculeus shorter than vesicule or, at most, of the same length; segments of metasoma and stinger with only a few hairs.

Pectines: Inner fulcra with one hair or bristle; females with 23–29 denticles, males with 32–38 denticles.

Pedipalps: Femur granulate dorsally; tibia smooth, with distinct inner and dorsal inner crests, median-dorsal crests always indistinct at their base; 'inner length' of tibia equal to width of tibia or less; hand broad, wider than tibia and smooth except on inner side; fingers slightly curved, recess and hump of varying size; movable finger with 12–15 series of denticles.

Walking Legs: Outer tooth of basitarsal spur bifurcate at base, sometimes simple on some legs.

Systematic Remarks: Linnean specimens of *Scorpio australis* examined by Thorell were found to be identical to *Androctonus funestus* (cited in Kraepelin 1895 : 8). However, Pocock (1895 : 306) doubted Thorell's determination.

The two species *A. libycus* and *A. melanophysa* are at present considered to be the two sexes of the same species, the first a female and the second a male (possibly a juvenile to judge from the drawing).

Vachon (1958) distinguished three subspecies according to their colour: *A. australis australis,* uniformly yellow; *A. a. libycus,* body yellow, end of metasoma black; *A. a. hector,* body yellow, hand of pedipalp and end of metasoma dark brown. Comparison of specimens from North Africa, Egypt, Arabia (Jidda, Hadhramaut, Muscat) and Sinai showed that, except for the slight differences in colour, there are no morphological differences. Many specimens are bleached by long preservation in alcohol and it is impossible to distinguish the subspecies. All shades of colour may be found even in fresh material. Thus, unless other diagnostic characters are used, it seems preferable to refrain from assigning subspecific names (the Sinai specimens would have to be determined as *libycus*). A description of the specimens from Sinai is given below.

Androctonus australis from Sinai

Figs. 39–42; Map 2

Coloration: Body and hand of pedipalp of adult yellow; posterior part of fifth segment of metasoma (mainly on ventral side) and stinger black.

Metasoma: Segments 3 and 4 of same width, both wider than segment 1; fourth segment longer than wide or as long as wide; fifth segment distinctly longer than wide; latero-dorsal crests of anterior segments with large separate granules, granules fused in anterior part of posterior segments, crests of fifth segment posteriorly in the

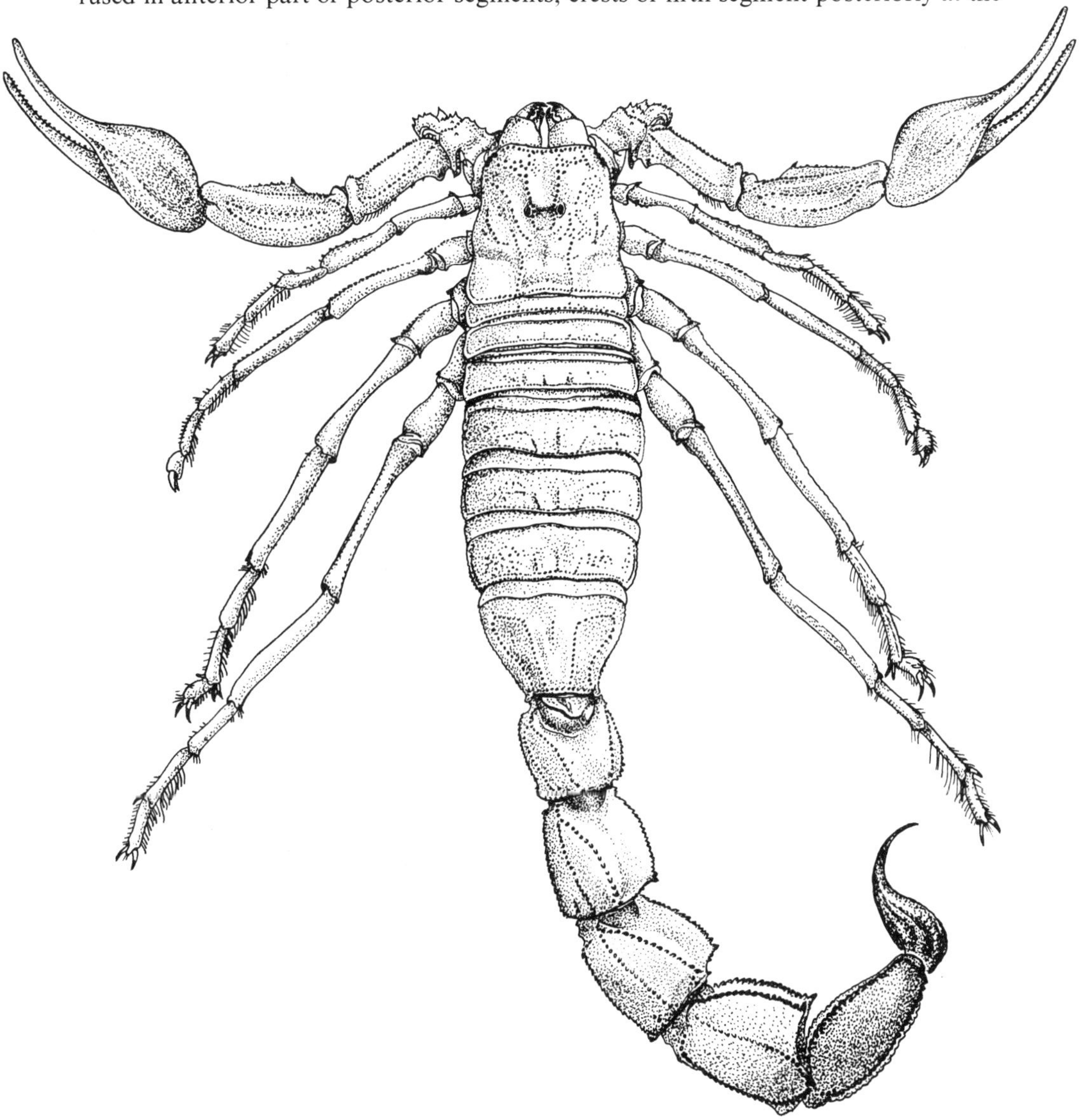

Fig. 39: *Androctonus australis* (Linnaeus, 1758)
Male from Rās Abū Rudeis (972/814), Sinai (Sc. 1730); total length 88 mm

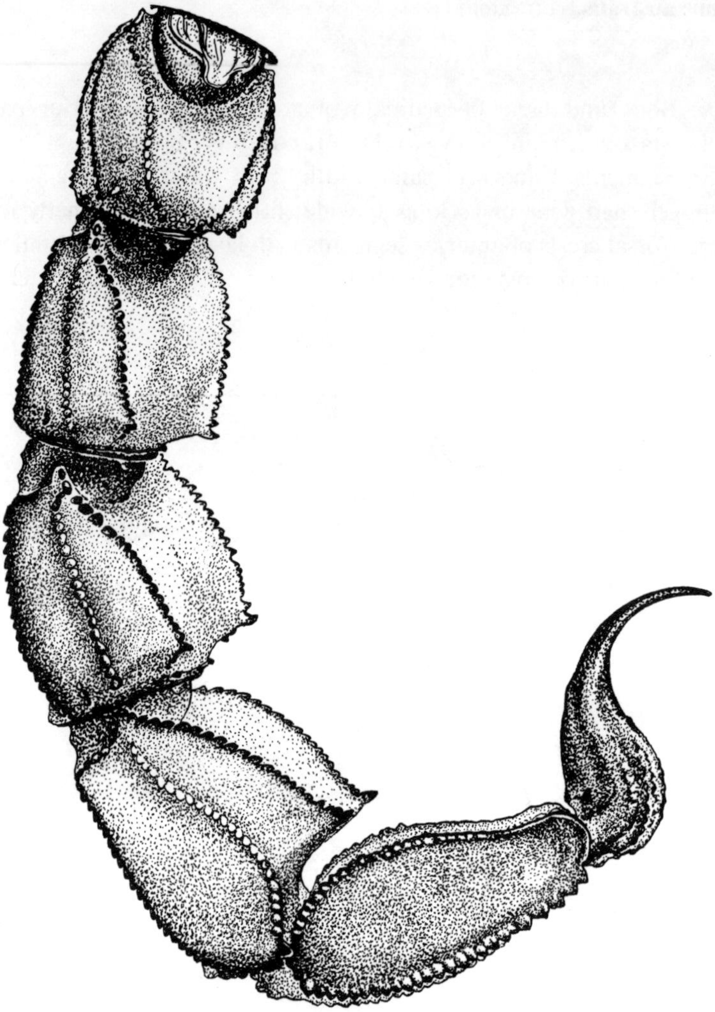

Fig. 40: *Androctonus australis* (Linnaeus, 1758). Metasoma, length 52 mm

form of raised lines without separate granules; intermediary crests of second segment with 3–8 granules, of third segment with 2–3 granules; latero-central crests of fifth segment with medium-sized, regular teeth which increase little in size posteriorly and extend to the anal margin; aculeus shorter than vesicule including pedicel but longer than width of vesicule; fifth segment 1.4–1.6 times wider than vesicule and 1.8–1.9 times wider than pedicel.

Pectines: In females extending to coxo-trochanteral articulation of leg IV, with 25–27 denticles; males with 31–35 denticles.

Pedipalps: Femur 2.5–3.0 times longer than wide and with accessory bristles distally on the outside; tibia 2.0–2.5 times longer than wide, without accessory bristles; median-dorsal crests with almost fused granules; latero-dorsal crests indistinct,

41

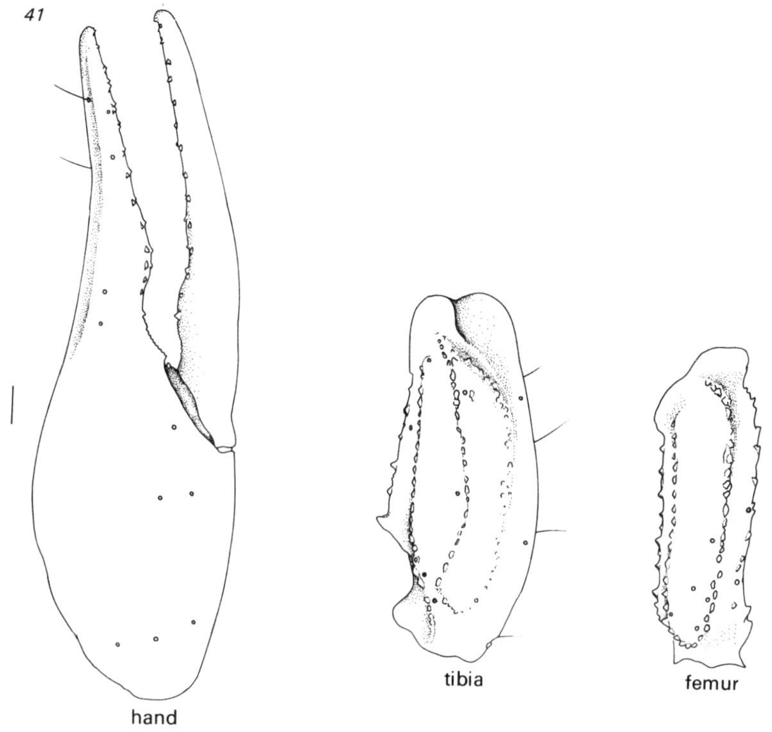

42

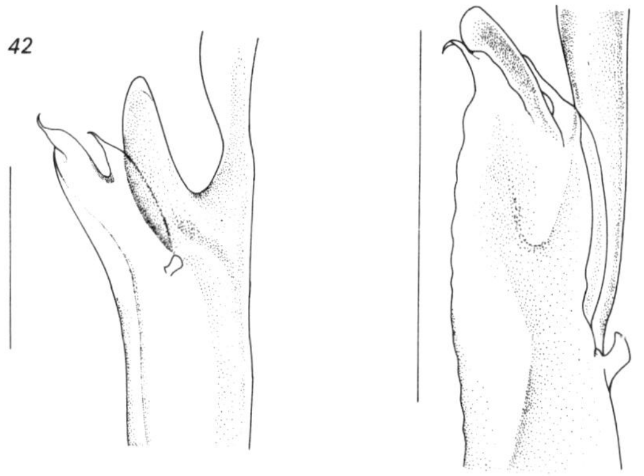

Figs. 41–42: *Androctonus australis* (Linnaeus, 1758). 41. pedipalp, arrangement of trichobothria; 42. paraxial organ, form of lobes at base of flagellum; scale-lines 1 mm

slightly indicated only distally; fingers thick, with large recess and hump, longer than prosoma and less than twice as long as hand; movable finger with 14–15 series of denticles.

Walking Legs: Outer tooth of basitarsal spur usually bifurcate distally; outer tooth of basitarsal spur of leg IV with 9–10 bristles; dorsal comb of basitarsus of leg III with 16–18 bristles.

Measurements (mm): *Female*. Adult, Sinai, Mitla Pass (No. Sc. 966). Total length 100; prosoma 11, mesosoma 29, metasoma 60. Segments of metasoma: first L6.2, W7.2, H6.0; second 7.2–7.5–6.5; third 7.5–7.8–7.3; fourth 8.2–7.8–7.1; fifth 9.0–7.2–6.5. Vesicule (including pedicel) L6.0, W5.0; pedicel of vesicule W3.9; aculeus (damaged) L5.4. Pedipalps: femur L8.7, W3.4; tibia L10.7, W4.7; hand L7.3, W5.9; movable finger L12.7. Number of denticles of pectine 25–27.

Male. Adult, Sinai, Rās Abū Rudeis (No. Sc. 1730). Total length 88; prosoma 10, mesosoma 26, metasoma 52. Segments of metasoma: first L5.7, W6.5, H5.8; second 6.1–6.8–6.1; third 7.1–7.5–6.7; fourth 7.5–7.5–6.7; fifth 8.1–6.6–5.7. Vesicule (including pedicel) L5.5, W4.2; pedicel of vesicule W3.6; aculeus L4.8. Pedipalps: femur L8.2, W2.7; tibia L10, W4.2; hand L6.5, W5.8; movable finger L11.7. Number of denticles of pectine 32–33.

Distribution: Northern Africa, Arabia (records from the British Museum): Jidda, Hadhramaut, Muscat.

Sinai (Map 2; p. 29): References of previous records from Sinai are summarized in the Appendix on Distribution. *Androctonus australis* is found along the western shores of Sinai, from the area of the Mitla Pass and southwards. The species also extends to the southern parts of the eastern shores of Sinai.

Gough & Hirst (1927) mention a specimen from 'Gaza'. We have not yet found this species in Israel.

Ecological Notes: *Androctonus australis* is well known in North Africa, and there is abundant information on its habitats and the composition of its venom. However, nothing is known about this species in our area.

Androctonus amoreuxi (Audouin, [1827])

Scorpio amoreuxii Audouin, [1827], *Description de l'Égypte*, Paris, 22 : 410, pl. 8, fig. 2. Type Locality: Egypt.

Androctonus (*Prionurus*) *citrinus* Hemprich & Ehrenberg, 1829, *Berolini ex officina Academica*: 120, pl. 2, fig. 2. Type Locality: Upper Egypt and Sudan.

Prionurus citrinus—. Pocock, 1895, *J. Linn. Soc.* (*Zool.*) *Lond.*, 25 : 306–307.

Buthus (*Prionurus*) *citrinus*—. Pocock, 1899, *Proc. Zool. Soc. Lond.*: 834.

Buthus australis var. *citrina*—. Kraepelin, 1899, *Das Tierreich*, 8. Lief., Berlin : 16.

Buthus (*Prionurus*) *baluchicus* Pocock, 1900, *Fauna of British India*, London, Taylor & Francis: 16. Type Locality: northern Baluchistan; in the British Museum (Natural History); examined.

Buthus deserticola Birula, 1903, *Bull. Acad. Imp. Sci. St.-Pétersbourg*. (5) 19(3) : 108–110. Type Locality: southern Algeria.

Buthus amoureuxi—. Birula, 1903, *Bull. Acad. Imp. Sci. St.-Pétersbourg*, (5) 19(3) : 110–112.

Buthus (*Prionurus*) *amoreuxi*—. Birula, 1908, *Sber. Akad. Wiss. Wien*, 117(2; 1) : 134–138.

Prionurus amoreuxi—. Pallary, 1925, *Archs Inst. Pasteur Algér.*, 3(1) : 57.

Buthus (*Hottentotta*) *hebraeus* Werner, 1935, *Zool. Anz.*, 109(7/8) : 212. Type Locality: Israel.

Androctonus amoreuxi—. Vachon, 1948, *Archs Inst. Pasteur Algér.*, 26(4) ; 464.

Androctonus amoreuxi baluchicus—. Vachon, 1958, *Vidensk. Meddr. Dansk Naturh. Foren.*, 120 : 125.

Coloration: Yellow or olive- to chocolate-brown; pedipalps and posterior segments of metasoma of the same colour as the body or darker, according to the subspecies. *Size*: Medium-sized, 6–9 cm long.
Prosoma: Densely granulate, with large or small granules, granules slightly larger anteriorly; crests sometimes distinct; median-ocular crests not reaching anterior margin of prosoma; median eyes situated slightly anterior to middle; lateral eyes small and distinct.
Mesosoma: Tergites sparsely granulate, more granulate laterally; crests distinct from third segment, sometimes with 2–3 granules on first or second segment; anterior sternites smooth, mat, third sternite slightly shagreened above spiracles, sixth sternite sometimes with slightly indicated, smooth lateral crests; seventh sternite smooth or slightly shagreened laterally, with four smooth or granulate crests; sternites with a few bristles.
Metasoma: Moderately thick, relatively little concave dorsally, fifth segment almost plane; first segment wider than long, rarely longer than wide; segments 2–5 longer than wide; third segment about as wide as segment 1; fourth segment narrower than segment 1 or of the same width; dorsal crests of segments 1–4 raised posteriorly, sometimes only slightly; segments smooth dorsally, sometimes with a few granules in dorsal groove on first segment and in spaces between dorsal and latero-dorsal crests; intermediary crests with only a few granules in posterior part of segment, sometimes extending midway along second segment or slightly further; sides of segments smooth except for slightly granulate or shagreened sides of fifth and sometimes fourth segment; ventral crests of segments 1–4 smooth, granulate or with fused granules; anterior segments smooth ventrally; posterior segments shagreened or slightly granulate; fifth segment long and slender, latero-ventral crests with teeth which increase in size posteriorly; fifth segment with 3–4 distinct lateral anal lobes, sometimes also with 3–4 small denticles; aculeus of varying length relative to vesicule; segments of metasoma and stinger with the usual number or only a few hairs.
Pectines: Inner fulcra with one fine hair; females with 18–29 denticles, males with 27–33 denticles.
Pedipalps: Femur granulate dorsally; tibia smooth, sometimes slightly shagreened dorsally, without accessory bristles; hand smooth, without crests, sometimes broad; fingers slightly curved, with recess and hump of varying size at base; movable finger with 11–16 series of denticles, inner and outer accessory teeth large.
Walking Legs: Outer tooth of basitarsal spur usually simple, rarely bifurcate on some legs.
Systematic Remarks: The description and drawing of *Scorpio amoreuxi*, published by Audouin in Savigny, are not diagnostic. However, most authors consider it identical to *A. citrinus* Hemprich & Ehrenberg, 1829.
The date of Audouin's work is problematic. The figures (pl. 8) are dated 1806–1811. According to Bonnet (1945: 551), the plates were published by Savigny in 1817. The text with the same plates was published, according to Bonnet, in two editions: the first in 1825 and the second in 1827. We cannot decide which of these dates is correct and therefore place the date in brackets. Most authors give the year 1827

for arachnids mentioned in this publication, a date which in any case precedes the publication of Hemprich & Ehrenberg.

Androctonus amoreuxi has a wide distribution from Senegal to Egypt and Sudan, to the southern border of Lebanon and to Afghanistan in the east. Until recently the information available about *A. amoreuxi* was rather limited. Vachon (1948) described *A. amoreuxi* from North Africa, but he mentions the possible occurrence of other subspecies in this area. Pocock described two species from Pakistan and Afghanistan, *finitimus* (1897) and *baluchicus* (1900). These were believed by Birula (1917) to be *A. crassicauda*. Vachon (1948) combined them with *A. australis*, and later (1958) placed them in *A. amoreuxi*. Examination of the type of *finitimus* proved that it is a different species. *Buthus hebraeus* was described from Israel by Werner (1935) and placed in the subgenus *Hottentotta*, but Vachon (1958) placed it in *A. amoreuxi*. Comparison of material from North Africa, Egypt and Sudan with specimens from Israel proved that *hebraeus* is a subspecies of *A. amoreuxi*.

Specimens of *A. a. amoreuxi* from Africa differ from *A. a. hebraeus* mainly in the following characters: first segment of metasoma wider than or as wide as fourth segment; aculeus about as long as vesicule, rarely longer; hand, also in female, wider than tibia and usually with a recess and hump at base of finger.

According to Vachon's (1958) rediscription of *A. a. baluchicus* from Afghanistan, this form differs from *A. a. hebraeus* as follows: colour chocolate-brown, posterior segments of metasoma and stinger dark; segments 3 and 4 as wide as segment 1; aculeus longer than stinger; segments of metasoma with only a few hairs; width of tibia of pedipalp less than 'inner length' of tibia; hand only slightly longer than wide and with only a small recess and hump at base of fingers.

Androctonus amoreuxi hebraeus (Werner, 1935)

Figs. 43–46; Map 2

Buthus (Hottentotta) hebraeus Werner, 1935, *Zool. Anz.*, 109(7/8): 212. Type Locality: Tel Aviv, Israel.

Androctonus amoreuxi hebraeus—. Vachon, 1958, *Vidensk. Meddr. Dansk Naturh. Foren.*, 120: 124.

Coloration: Body, pedipalps and legs yellow or olive-brown. *Size*: 6–9 cm.

Prosoma: Median-ocular crests with separate granules, except for part with fused granules between median eyes; median eyes separated from each other by about twice their diameter.

Metasoma: All segments wider than high; third segment slightly wider than segment 1 in males and slightly narrower in females; fourth segment distinctly longer than wide and narrower than segment 1 in both sexes; fifth segment 1.7 times longer than wide and 2.2 times longer than high; dorsal crests of segments 1–4 with separate granules, sometimes with fused granules, except for the larger granule at the end; latero-dorsal crests with separate or with fused granules, mainly on posterior segments, crests of fifth segment in the form of lines and sometimes indistinct; inter-

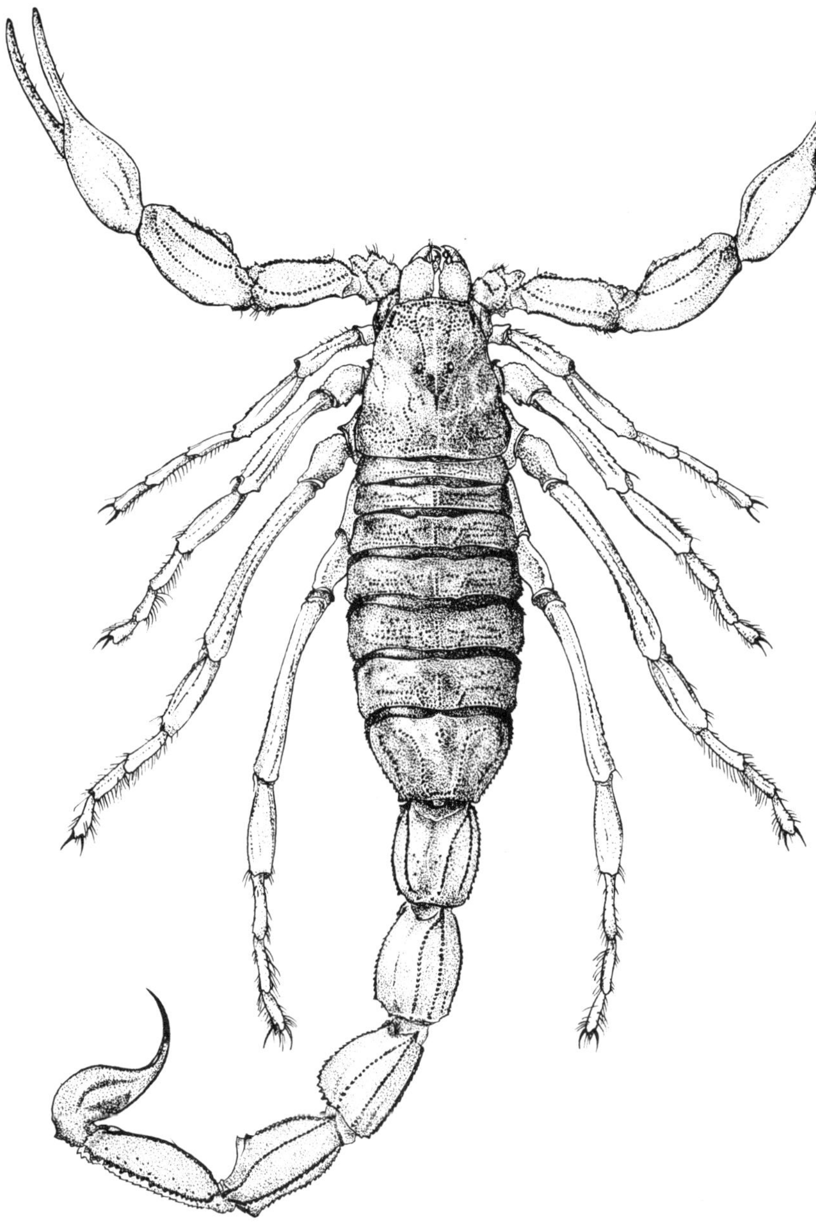

Fig. 43: *Androctonus amoreuxi hebraeus* (Werner, 1935)
Male from Naḫal Poleg (187/135), Israel (Sc. 1861); total length 69 mm

mediary crests of second segment of slightly varying length, with 2–9 granules; intermediary crests of third segment with 2–5 granules, sometimes with a few additional small granules; ventral crests of first segment smooth, granules more distinct and separate posteriorly; axial and ventral crests of fifth segment distinct, sometimes ventral crests indistinct; latero-ventral crests of fifth segment with distinct teeth

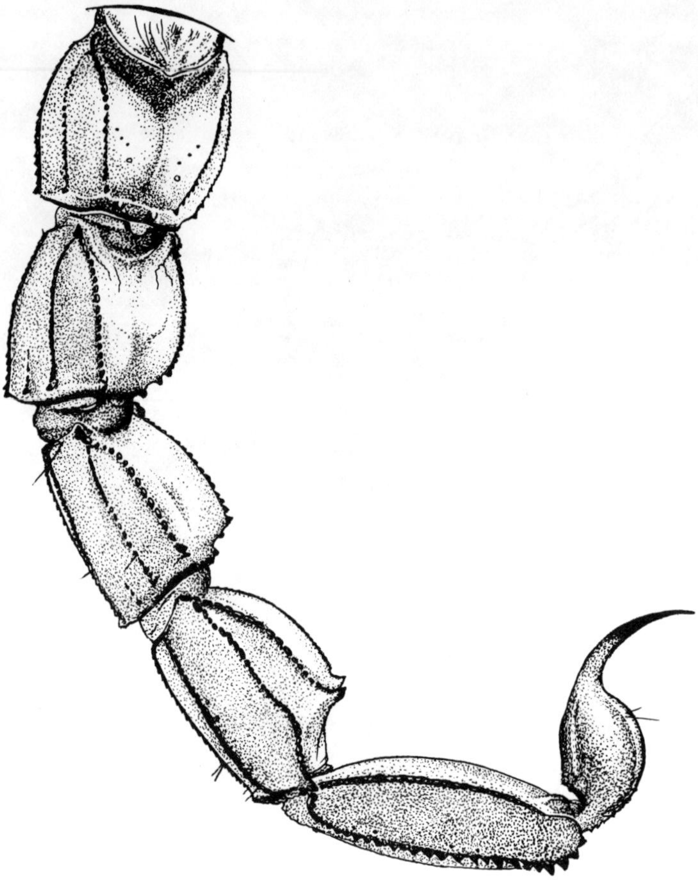

Fig. 44: *Androctonus amoreuxi hebraeus* (Werner, 1935). Metasoma, length 45 mm

throughout extending to anal margin, with pointed and larger teeth in posterior part; aculeus shorter than vesicule (including pedicel) but distinctly longer than width of vesicule; fifth segment 1.3–1.5 times wider than vesicule and 1.7–2.1 times wider than pedicel of vesicule; segments of metasoma and stinger with the usual number of hairs.

Pectines: In females not extending to coxo-trochanteral articulation of leg IV, with 18–25 denticles; males with 26–33 denticles.

Pedipalps: Femur 2.2–2.5 times longer than wide and with numerous accessory bristles distally on the outside; tibia twice as long as wide and 1.3–1.5 times wider than 'inner length'; dorsal-inner crests granulate or smooth, median-dorsal and latero-dorsal crests smooth and indistinct; hand very broad, 1.2–1.4 times longer than wide; hand about as wide as tibia in males, slightly narrower than tibia in females; hand smooth also on inner side and about twice as long as 'inner length' of tibia; fingers very thick, with a large recess and hump at base; fingers 1.5–1.8

45

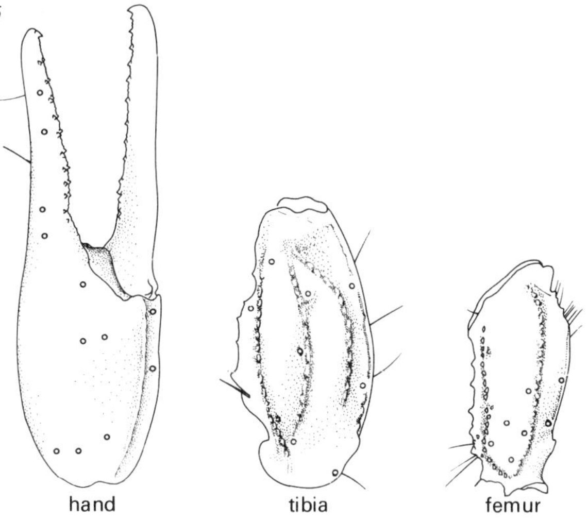

46

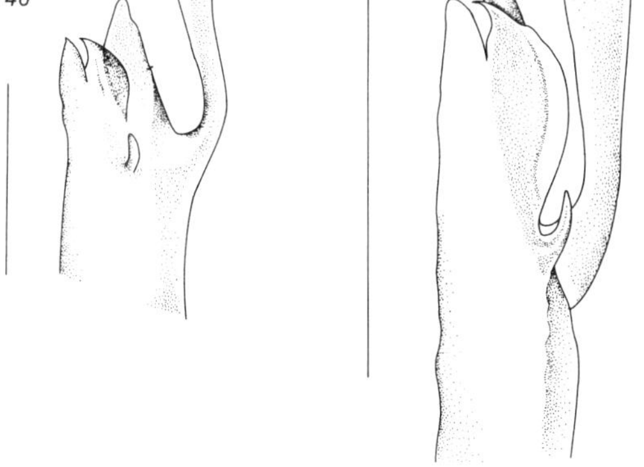

Figs. 45–46: *Androctonus amoreuxi hebraeus* (Werner, 1935)
45. pedipalp, arrangement of trichobothria; 46. paraxial organ, form of lobes at base of flagellum; scale-lines 1 mm

times longer than hand and about as long as prosoma; movable finger with 11–12 series of denticles.

Walking Legs: Outer tooth of basitarsal spur simple, sometimes with basal bifurcation on some legs; outer tooth of basitarsal spur of leg IV with 10–18 bristles; dorsal comb of basitarsus of leg III with 15–21 bristles.

Measurements (mm): There is a morphometric cline from north to south in this subspecies. Northern specimens are smaller; females usually have 18–22 denticles on the pectines and males 27–29 denticles. Specimens from southern Israel and Sinai are larger; females usually with 23–24 denticles on the pectines and males with 29–33 denticles, but there are exceptions.

Female. Adult, 'En Gedi, Naẖal 'Arugot (No. Sc. 1194). Total length 77; prosoma 8, mesosoma 25, metasoma 44. Segments of metasoma: first L4.5, W4.9, H4.0; second 5.4–4.8–4.1; third 5.6–4.7–4.3; fourth 6.1–4.4–4.0; fifth 7.2–4.2–3.3. Vesicule (including pedicel) L4.8, W3.1; pedicel of vesicule W2.3; aculeus L3.9. Pedipalps: femur L5.5, W2.4; tibia L7.4, W3.7; hand L4.5, W3.3; movable finger L7.9. Number of denticles of pectine 19–21.

Male. Adult, Ẕe'elim (No. Sc. 294). Total length 70; prosoma 8, mesosoma 17, metasoma 45. Segments of metasoma: first L4.5, W5.0, H4.0; second 5.6–5.0–4.0; third 5.9–5.1–4.1; fourth 6.5–4.7–3.9; fifth 7.7–4.5–3.4. Vesicule (including pedicel) L4.7, W3.0; pedicel of vesicule W2.2; aculeus L4.1. Pedipalps: femur L5.6, W2.4; tibia L7.3, W3.7; hand L5.0, W4.1; movable finger L7.4. Number of denticles of pectine 28–28.

Distribution, Israel and Sinai (Map 2; p. 29): References of previous records from Israel are summarized in the Appendix on Distribution. *Androctonus amoreuxi* was formerly unknown from Sinai. Records of *A. amoreuxi* are from a narrow zone along the Coastal Plain from about 'Akko (Acre) to Gaza, and along the western shores of Sinai from Qantara to Abū Rudeis. It probably also occurs in northern Sinai. In the Negev it extends to Be'er Sheva' and 'En Gedi along the Dead Sea.

Ecological Notes: *Androctonus amoreuxi hebraeus* inhabits mainly sandy areas and is quite common. It occurs on sand dunes in the Coastal Plain and desert, on brown-red sandy soils and on loess-sandy soils. It moves rather slowly. It is sometimes found on steep slopes of drifting dunes and also in burrows. Parturition usually in June–July.

Genus LEIURUS Hemprich & Ehrenberg, 1829

Berolini ex officina Academica: 118

Leiurus—. Vachon, 1949, *Archs. Inst. Pasteur Algér.*, 27(1): 83.

Type Species: *Androctonus* (*Leiurus*) *quinquestriatus* Hemprich & Ehrenberg, 1829; subsequent designation by Vachon, 1949.

Diagnosis: Prosoma with latero-central crests united posteriorly with median-posterior crests, forming a lyra-shaped figure; anterior tergites of mesosoma with five crests; always four denticles under apical tooth of movable finger of pedipalp.

Prosoma: Granulate, with distinctly granulate crests; median-central crests isolated and forming an H-shaped figure; latero-posterior crests short and distinct; posterior margin of prosoma slightly concave in the middle; median eyes large, separated from each other by more than their diameter.

Mesosoma: Two anterior tergites with five, other tergites with at least three distinctly granulate crests; posterior end of crests attenuated.

Metasoma: Slender, slightly narrowing posteriorly; anterior segments concave dorsally, posterior segment slightly convex; short intermediary crests only on second and third segments; segments 1–4 with distinctly granulate dorsal crests; latero-

ventral crests of fifth segment with irregular granules; lateral anal lobes of fifth segment distinct; vesicule relatively narrow, without subaculear tubercle.
Pectines: Inner fulcra with short, sclerotized point.
Pedipalps: Crests of tibia slightly indistinct; hand smooth or almost smooth; finger with an outer accessory denticle near each series of denticles.
Walking Legs: Outer tooth of basitarsal spur simple, with only a few bristles; basitarsi of three anterior legs with a comb of bristles dorsally; sole of tarsi with short hairs or bristles.
Review of Genus: Kraepelin (1891) considered *Leiurus* a synonym of the genus *Buthus*. Vachon (1949) established *Leiurus* as a separate genus with only one species. *Leiurus quinquestriatus* has a wide distribution, from Algeria to Egypt, Somalia and Sudan, to the Arabian Peninsula in the east and to Lebanon and Syria in the north.

Leiurus quinquestriatus Hemprich & Ehrenberg, 1829

?*Scorpio occitanus* Audouin, [1827], *Description de l'Égypte*, Paris, 22 : 410, pl. 8, fig. 1 (non Amoreux, 1789).
Androctonus (*Leiurus*) *quinquestriatus* Hemprich & Ehrenberg, 1829, *Berolini ex officina Academica*: 118, pl. 1, fig. 5. Type Locality: Egypt.
Buthus beccari Simon, 1882, *Annali Mus. Civ. Stor. Nat. Genova*, 18 : 246. Type Locality: Yemen (Moka).
Buthus quinquestriatus—. Kraepelin, 1891, *Jb. Hamb. Wiss. Anst.*, 8 : 58.
Leiurus quinquestriatus—. Vachon, 1949, *Archs. Inst. Pasteur Algér.*, 27(1) : 83.

Prosoma: Median-ocular crests distinct throughout or mixed anteriorly with adjacent granules; space between median-posterior crests smooth or granulate.
Mesosoma: Tergites completely granulate; granules between crests small, large and coarse laterally; sternites 4–7 with four crests.
Metasoma: Intermediary crests of second and third segments extending over posterior part of segments; ventral crests of second and third segments regularly or irregularly granulate; ventral crests of fourth segment regularly granulate; fifth segment with three distinct lateral anal lobes; aculeus slightly curved and of varying length relative to length of vesicule.
Pectines: Extending in both sexes to or (mainly in males) beyond coxo-trochanteral articulation of leg IV.
Systematic Remarks: *Leiurus quinquestriatus* was assumed to have two subspecies, *L. q. aculeatus* (= *L. q. quinquestriatus*) and *L. q. brachycentrus*. The first subspecies occurs in Africa and Sinai and is most common in Egypt. The second was based on a single specimen from Jidda (Gumfudam), Arabia. Examination of numerous specimens from Arabia, including some from Jidda, proved that this subspecies is not valid. *Buthus beccari*, described by Simon (1882, 1890), was stated to differ from *L. quinquestriatus* in that its median-ocular crests extended to the anterior margin of the prosoma. Kraepelin (1891) showed that this character is variable, even in a small population. Kraepelin (1891, 1899) and Birula (1908, 1917) considered *B. beccari* a synonym of *L. q. brachycentrus* (= *L. q. quinquestriatus*).

Birula (1908) recorded a separate subspecies from Israel, *L. q. hebraeus,* in addition to the Egyptian *L. q. quinquestriatus.* Comparison of large collections of specimens from Africa and Asia confirmed the validity of this subspecies. Birula (1908) described *L. q. libycus* from Libya, but Vachon (1949) found this unjustified. Pohl (1967) described another subspecies from Israel, *L. q. voelschowi,* based on colour differences. Examination of numerous specimens from Israel showed that this subspecies is not justified (Levy et al., 1970).

Leiurus quinquestriatus hebraeus (Birula, 1908)
Figs. 47–51; Map 3

Buthus quinquestriatus hebraeus Birula, 1908, *Sber. Akad. Wiss. Wien,* 117(2; 1): 124–129. Type Locality: Wadi 'Arrud, 'Arabia Petraea' (southern Israel or Jordan).
Leiurus quinquestriatus voelschowi Pohl, 1967, *Annln Naturh. Mus. Wien,* 70: 209–215. Type Locality: Israel.

Coloration: Body and appendages light yellow to orange-brown; fifth segment of metasoma usually black in young specimens, occasionally only slightly darker or of the same colour as other segments in adults. *Size*: 5.5–9.5 cm.
Prosoma: Rarely a few granules outside of median-central crests, but forming no connection to other crests; space between median-posterior crests sparsely or densely granulate, often traversed by a pair of distinct crescents, with or without small granules.
Mesosoma: Sternum distinctly wider than long; crests of sternites 4–7 slightly raised, more coarsely granulate posteriorly.
Metasoma: Intermediary crests of second segment usually with 7–12 granules, sometimes extending beyond half of segment; intermediary crests of third segment usually with 4–7 granules, always shorter than half the segment; ventral crests of second and third segments irregularly granulate, with larger and coarser granules posteriorly (females with 14–26 granules, males with more); axial crest of fifth segment raised, usually with 15–19 granules, ventral crests with usually 5–8 distinct, isolated granules; pedicel of vesicule slightly wider than half width of vesicule; aculeus almost always shorter than vesicule, rarely as long as vesicule; aculeus usually distinctly longer than width of vesicule, rarely as long as the width and very rarely shorter.
Pectines: Females with 26–38 (usually 28–32) denticles, males with 31–43 (usually 33–36) denticles.
Pedipalps: Femur slender; fingers long, often longer in females than twice the length of the hand, rarely less than twice as long; fingers of males usually shorter than those of females, sometimes distinctly more than twice as long as hand, or less than twice as long; movable finger with 12–13 series of denticles.
Walking Legs: Outer tooth of basitarsal spur of leg IV with two bristles (rarely with 2–3 additional bristles); dorsal comb of basitarsus of leg III with 7–12 bristles.
Measurements (mm): *Female.* Adult, Hamakhtesh Hagadol (No. Sc. 767). Total length 80; prosoma 9, mesosoma 21, metasoma 50. Segments of metasoma: first

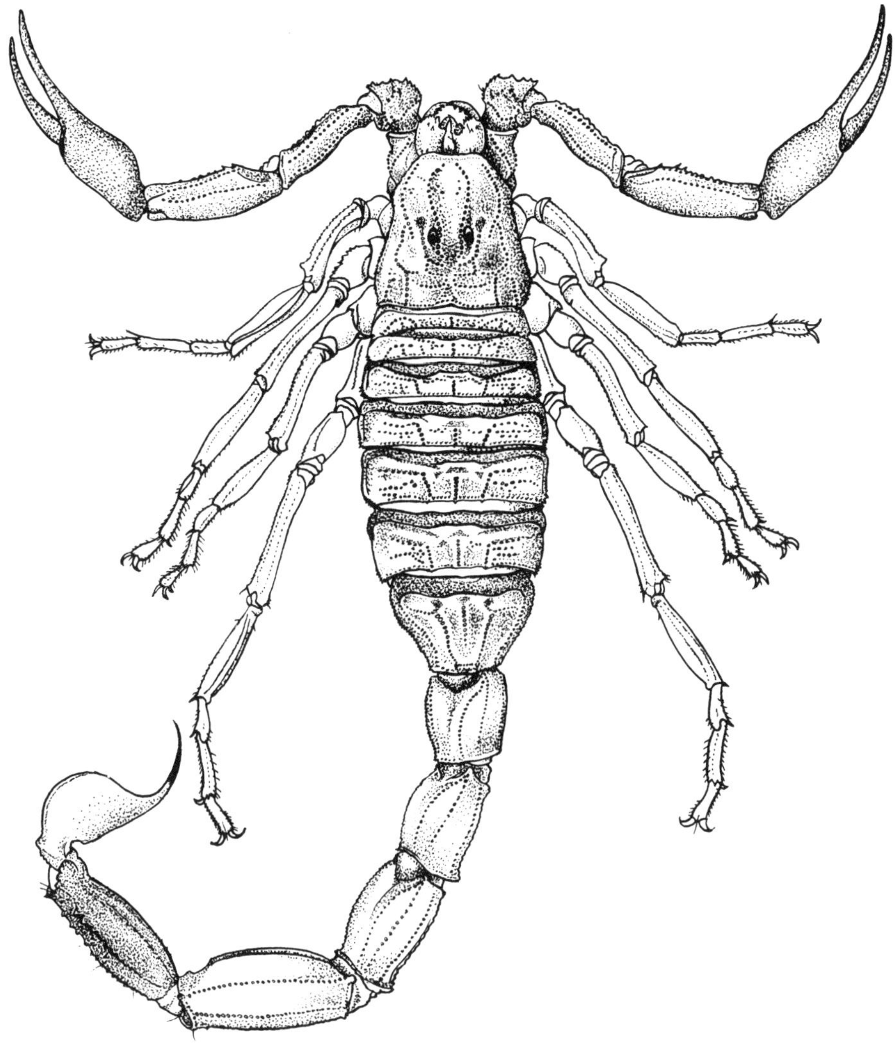

Fig. 47: *Leiurus quinquestriatus hebraeus* (Birula, 1908)
Male from Bet Guvrin, Israel (Sc. 1948); total length 68 mm

L5.5, W5.7, H5.0; second 6.8–5.0–4.7; third 7.0–4.9–4.7; fourth 7.4–4.6–4.5; fifth 8.8–4.5–4.0. Vesicule (without pedicel) L5.2, W4.2; pedicel L0.5, W2.2; aculeus L5.0. Pedipalps: femur L8.2, W2.5; tibia L9.5, W3.8; hand L5.4, W3.1; movable finger L12.1. Number of denticles of pectine 31–32.

Male. Adult, 'Arad (No. Sc. 1054). Total length 67; prosoma 7, mesosoma 16, metasoma 44. Segments of metasoma: first L4.4, W4.9, H3.1; second 5.7–4.3–3.8; third 5.9–4.0–3.6; fourth 6.6–3.8–3.4; fifth 7.4–3.5–2.9. Vesicule (without pedicel) L4.1, W3,1; pedicel L0.7, W1.9; aculeus L3.7, Pedipalps: femur L7.0, W2.0; tibia

48

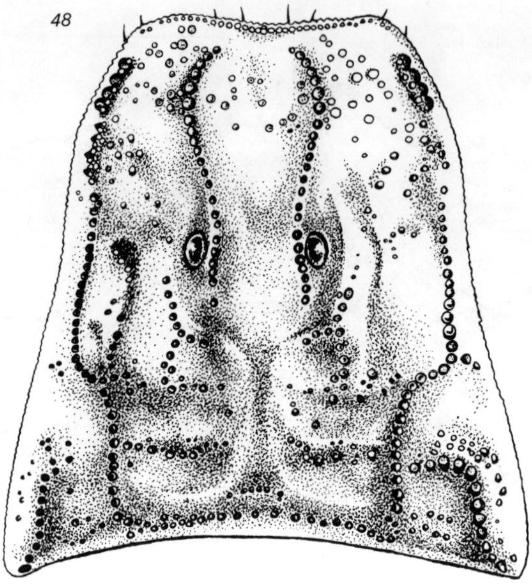

49

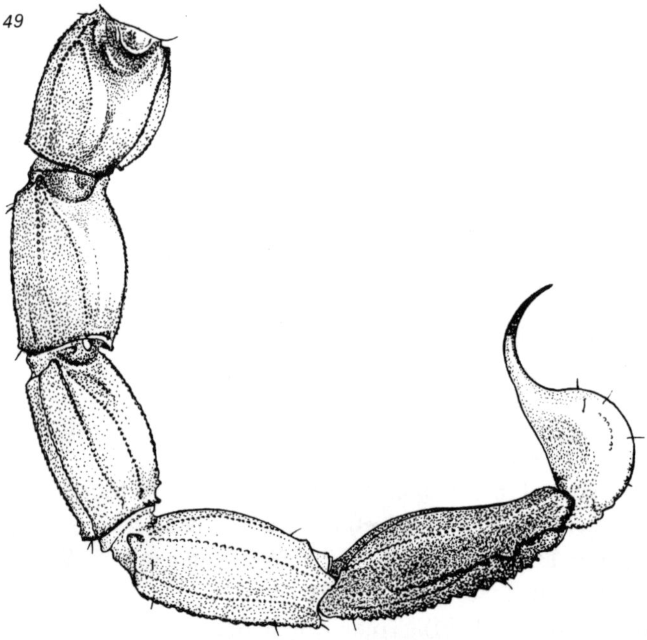

Figs. 48–49: *Leiurus quinquestriatus hebraeus* (Birula, 1908)
48. prosoma, length 6.5 mm; 49. metasoma, length 43 mm

50

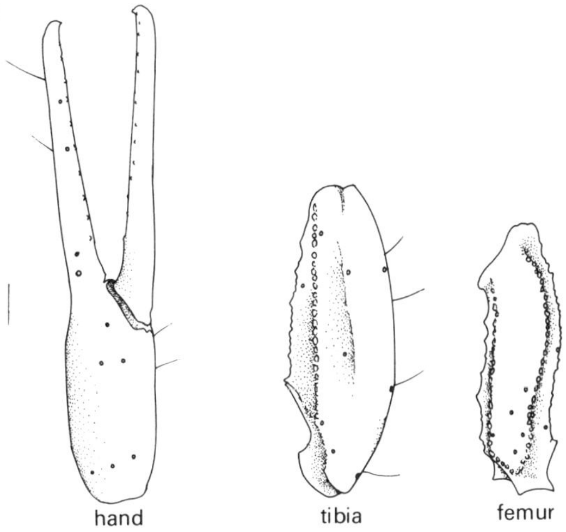

51

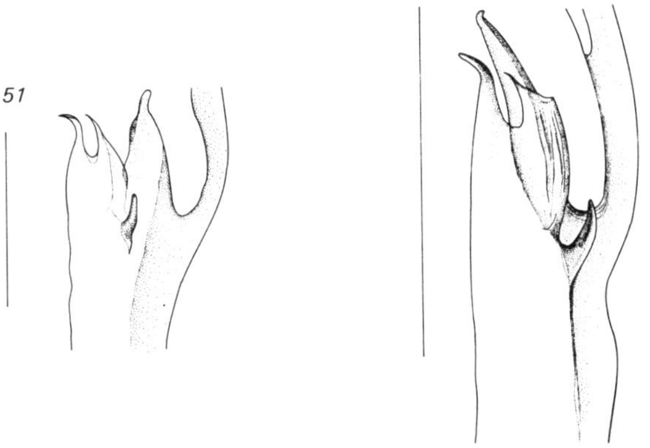

Figs. 50–51: *Leiurus quinquestriatus hebraeus* (Birula, 1908)
50. pedipalp, arrangement of trichobothria; 51. paraxial organ, form of lobes at base of flagellum; scale-lines 1 mm

L8.1, W2.7; hand L4.6, W2.6; movable finger L9.5. Number of denticles of pectine 34–35.
Distribution: The references of the following records are summarized in the Appendix on Distribution. Syria: east of Palmyra, Wadi Barada near Suk; additional records from the Muséum National, Paris: Doummar—*leg.* Kerville, 1911, determined by Simon as *B. europaeus,* Soueida–Gebel Druz, 60 km east of Homs; records from the British Museum: Road Homs–Damascus, Gebel Mazar. The line Homs–Palmyra is probably the northern border of *L. quinquestriatus.* Lebanon: the Muséum National, Paris, houses a specimen from El Kah, in the north. Jordan: Mafrak, Petra: record from the Muséum National, Paris: Wadi Deba‘ 100 km southeast of

Amman. Arabia: Jidda, Medina, Amarna, Yemen, Hadhramaut. Most specimens from Arabia in the British Museum clearly belong to *L. q. hebraeus*, but some slightly resemble *L. q. quinquestriatus* from Africa. However, these should not be considered a separate subspecies as they have characters intermediate between *L. q. hebraeus* and *L. q. quinquestriatus* such as those described for an exceptionally large specimen from the island of Senappir near the southeastern shores of Sinai (Levy et al., 1970). Another exceptional specimen in the British Museum, a female from Perim Island, clearly belongs to *L. q. hebraeus* but has an unusually small number (24–25) of denticles on the pectines.

Israel and Sinai (Map 3): There are numerous records of *L. quinquestriatus* from the north throughout Israel and Sinai. The species is absent, however, in a wide zone along the Mediterranean coast of Israel and northern Sinai.

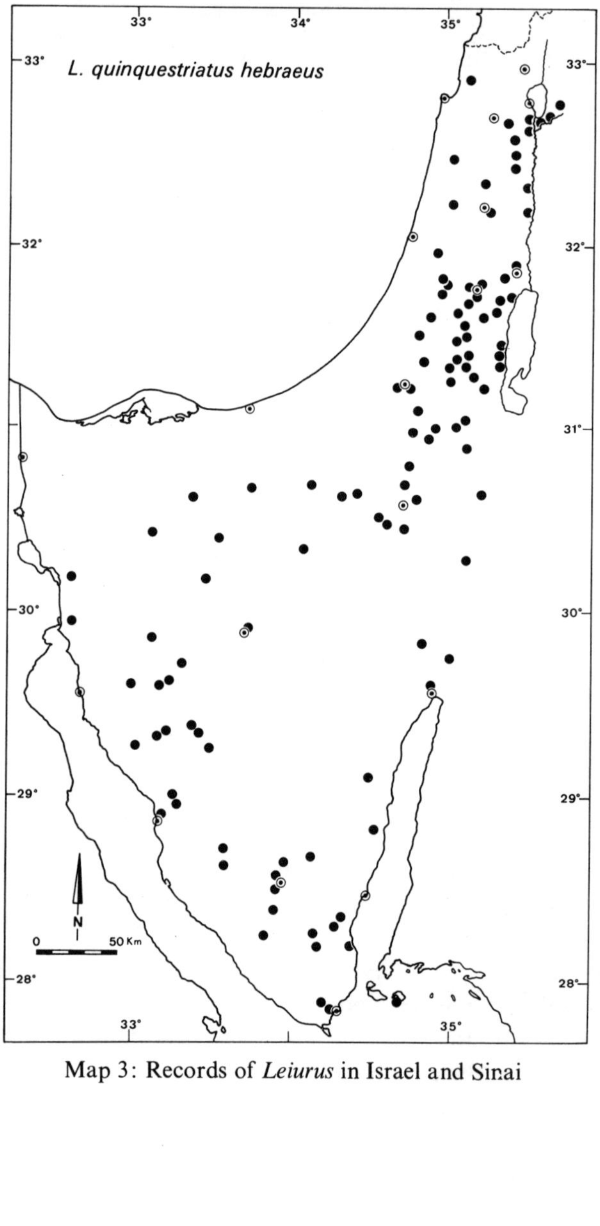

Map 3: Records of *Leiurus* in Israel and Sinai

Ecological Notes: *Leiurus quinquestriatus* is the most common species in this country, sometimes occurring in relatively dense populations. It is found on various types of soil: terra rossa, basalt, rendzina, loess and stony desert. It does not occur in the Coastal Plain, on Mount Carmel or in plains and valleys with sand dunes or heavy soil. It usually lives under small and large flat stones or in loosely built stone walls; it sometimes enters houses. It cleans and smooths its place under the stone. It occasionally digs a slightly oblique and wide burrow about 20 cm long. The two sexes are sometimes found together under the same stone. Parturition usually June–August; number of young 12–35. It is very agile and stings rapidly. It usually preys on large arthropods and climbs on shrubs and bushes. Its sting is dangerous to man and may cause death, especially in children (see also Introduction).

Genus BUTHOTUS Vachon, 1949

Archs Inst. Pasteur Algér., 27(2): 143–147

Type Species: *Buthus judaicus* Simon, 1872.

Diagnosis: Prosoma with median-central and median-posterior crests situated behind each other; sole of tarsi with spines.

Prosoma: Granulate, with granulate crests; latero-central crests separated from median-posterior crests; latero-posterior crests absent; posterior margin of prosoma almost straight; median eyes small, separated from each other by more than their diameter.
Mesosoma: Tergites granulate, with three crests at least from third segment onwards; crests of seventh sternite smooth or granulate.
Metasoma: Segments usually of the same width, concave dorsally; intermediary crests on second, third and sometimes also on fourth segment; segments 1–4 with distinct granulate dorsal crests; latero-ventral crests of fifth segment with regular, inconspicuous granules; lateral anal lobes of fifth segment not projecting; vesicule thick, rugose ventrally, without subaculear tubercle.
Pectines: Inner fulcra with short sclerotized point.
Pedipalps: Crests of tibia usually distinct; basal part of hand smooth or with indistinct crests; fingers with outer accessory denticles near all series of denticles; always four denticles under apical tooth of movable finger.
Walking Legs: Outer tooth of basitarsal spur simple, with only one or two hairs; basitarsus without a dorsal comb of bristles.

Review of Genus: *Buthotus* includes species which had previously been placed in the genus *Buthus*, group *Hottentotta*. The establishment of a *Hottentotta* group was probably due to the attempt by Kraepelin (1891) to assign all the forms in the genus *Buthus* to six 'species'. One of these, *B. hottentotta* (Fabricius, 1793) from Sierra Leone, included *B. judaicus* from Israel as a synonym. The term '*Hottentotta* group' was first used by Kraepelin (1895). Birula (1908 : 141, note) considered this group to be the subgenus *Hottentotta*, and later (Birula, 1927 : 82) presented arguments as to why *Hottentotta* should be considered a genus. However, he retained it as a subgenus, as did Werner (1934).

Because of the bare segments of the metasoma in *B. hottentotta*, in contrast to the dense pilosity of these segments in the other species of this group, Pallary (1938) established the genus *Dasyscorpio*, with *B. lutaudi* as type species. Vachon (1949) did not accept this and placed all species in the new genus *Buthotus*.

A list of species of the genus *Buthotus* was given by Vachon & Stockmann (1968). Twenty-one species and about a dozen subspecies are listed. The distribution extends over the whole of Africa and from the Mediterranean to Iran and India. Only one species, *B. judaicus*, occurs in our area.

Buthotus judaicus (Simon, 1872)

Figs. 52–56; Map 4

Buthus judaicus Simon, 1872, *Annls Soc. Ent. Fr.*, (5)2 : 252–254. Type Locality: Jerusalem.

Coloration: Body brownish black to greenish black; pedipalps and legs brown, end of fingers and legs light brown; pectines light. *Size*: 6–8 cm.

Prosoma: Densely granulate, mainly laterally; anterior margin slightly concave in the middle; median-ocular crests granulate, only area between median eyes smooth or with fused granules; median-posterior crests with distinct, separate granules, crests branching inwards into small granulate crests; space between median-posterior crests distinctly granulate, with small separate granules; space between median-ocular crests sometimes with a few small granules; median eyes separated from each other by about twice their diameter.

Mesosoma: Tergites densely granulate, mainly laterally; crests of tergites with distinct, separate granules; lateral crests directed obliquely outwards and slightly branched; space between oblique lateral crests and posterior margin of tergites with distinctly separate granules; sixth sternite without crests; seventh sternite with four indistinct, smooth or almost smooth crests.

Metasoma: Segments smooth dorsally, with only a few small sparse granules, females with slightly more numerous granules; all segments granulate laterally and ventrally, with small granules; crests of males usually less granulate than in females; all crests of males, except dorsal crests, smooth or with fused granules; granules of dorsal crests separate, slightly serrate and gradually increasing in size posteriorly, granule at the end the same size as the others; latero-dorsal crests of fifth segment usually indistinct; intermediary crests of third segment in males with 3–4 (slightly more in females) large, distinct granules and sometimes with a few more indistinct, small granules; ventral crests of females with fused or almost fused granules on segments 1–2, with almost fused or sometimes separate granules on segments 3–4; ventral crests of fifth segment with small, spaced granules; axial crest in females sometimes with distinct granules, crest usually indistinct anteriorly in males; latero-ventral crests of fifth segment of males smooth anteriorly, with distinctly separate

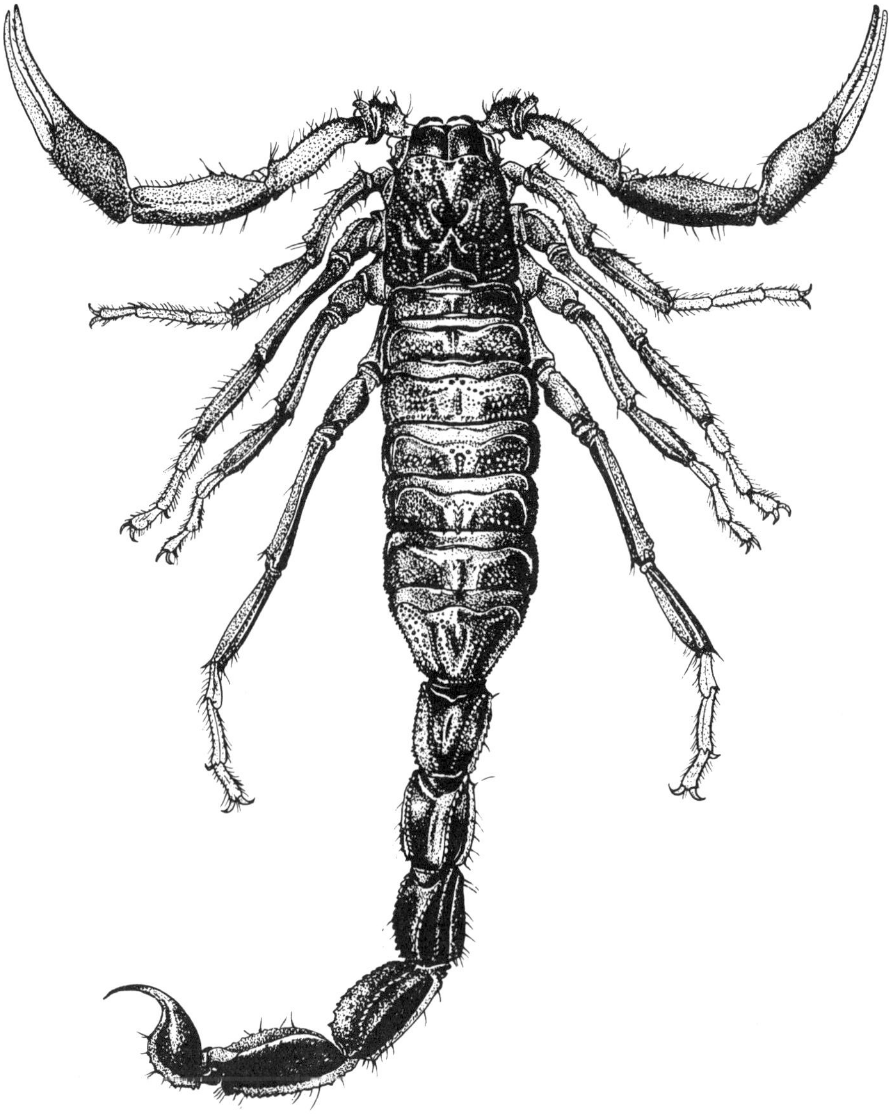

Fig. 52: *Buthotus judaicus* (Simon, 1872)
Male from Umm el Faḫm, Israel (Sc. 1973); total length 74 mm

granules in females; fifth segment distinctly wider than vesicule; aculeus distinctly shorter than vesicule without pedicel.

Pectines: Females with 22–27 (usually 24–25) denticles, males with 27–32 (usually 28–31) denticles.

Pedipalps: Crests of femur with distinct, separate granules, latero-dorsal crests usually indistinct at base; tibia smooth on outer side, dorsal crests distinct, rarely not granulate; median-dorsal crests smooth, inner crests granulate; tibia wider than

53

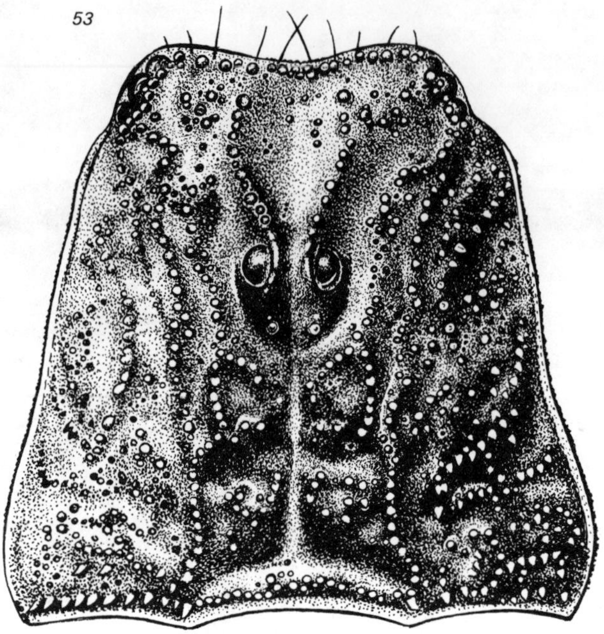

54

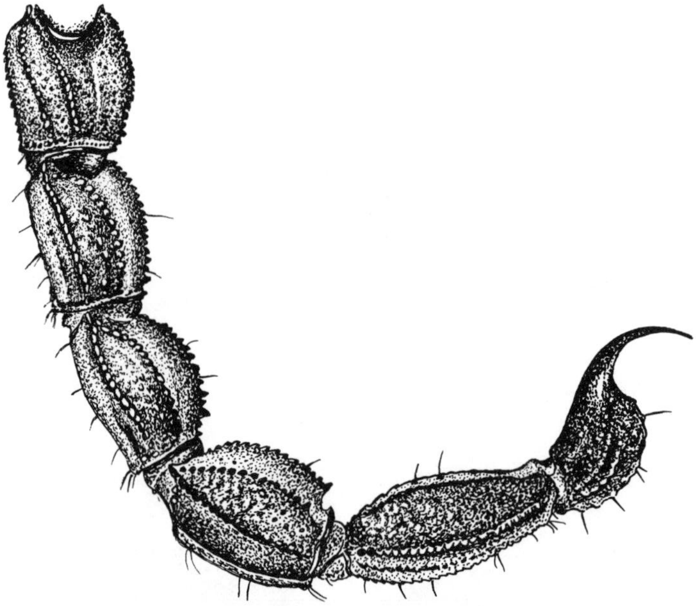

Figs. 53–54: *Buthotus judaicus* (Simon, 1872)
53. prosoma, length 6.9 mm; 54. metasoma, length 41 mm

55

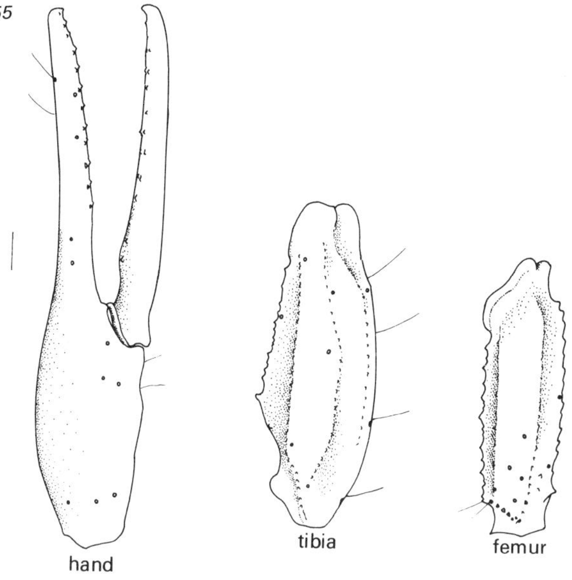

56

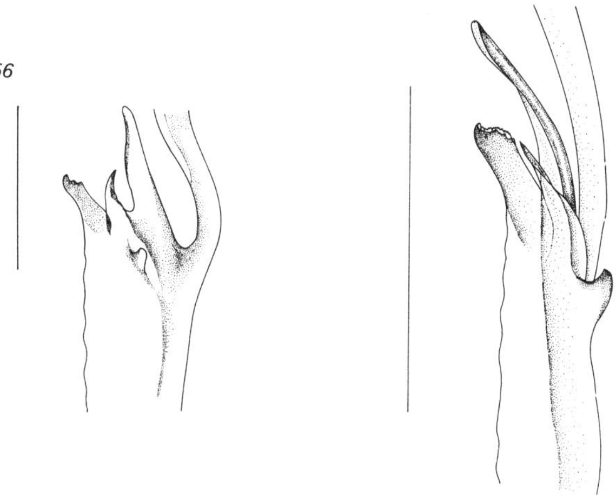

Figs. 55–56: *Buthotus judaicus* (Simon, 1872). 55. pedipalp, arrangement of trichobothria; 56. paraxial organ, form of lobes at base of flagellum; scale-lines 1 mm

hand or sometimes as wide as hand in males; hand smooth, without crests; fingers distinctly longer than prosoma; movable finger with 13–14 series of denticles.
Walking Legs: Outer tooth of basitarsal spur of leg III with one hair.
Measurements (mm): *Female*. Adult, Poriyya (No. Sc. 737). Total length 71; prosoma 7, mesosoma 21, metasoma 43. Segments of metasoma: first L4.1, W4.8, H4.0; second 5.0–4.5–4.0; third 5.3–4.5–4.0; fourth 5.9–4.2–3.9; fifth 7.6–4.2–3.8. Vesicule (without pedicel) L4.8, W3.3; pedicel W1.8; aculeus L4.0. Pedipalps: femur

L6.5, W2.0; tibia L8.0, W3.2; hand L4.5, W3.0; movable finger L8.9. Number of denticles of pectine 24–24.

Male. Adult, 'Avdon, Western Galilee (No. Sc. 743). Total length 68; prosoma 6, mesosoma 20, metasoma 42. Segments of metasoma: first L3.9, W4.2, H3.8; second 4.7–4.0–3.8; third 5.3–3.9–3.8; fourth 5.8–3.9–3.6; fifth 7.7–3.9–3.5. Vesicule (without pedicel) L4.0, W3.1; pedicel W1.7; aculeus L3.5. Pedipalps: femur L6.5, W1.9; tibia L7.6, W2.8; hand L4.5, W2.8; movable finger L8.4. Number of denticles of pectine 28–28.

Distribution: Turkey: Except for two females from Ala Cheir in Asia Minor (apparently in the southeast; Werner, 1902), there are no other records from localities in Turkey. Birula (1910, 1914, 1917) recorded *B. judaicus* from Turkey in general,

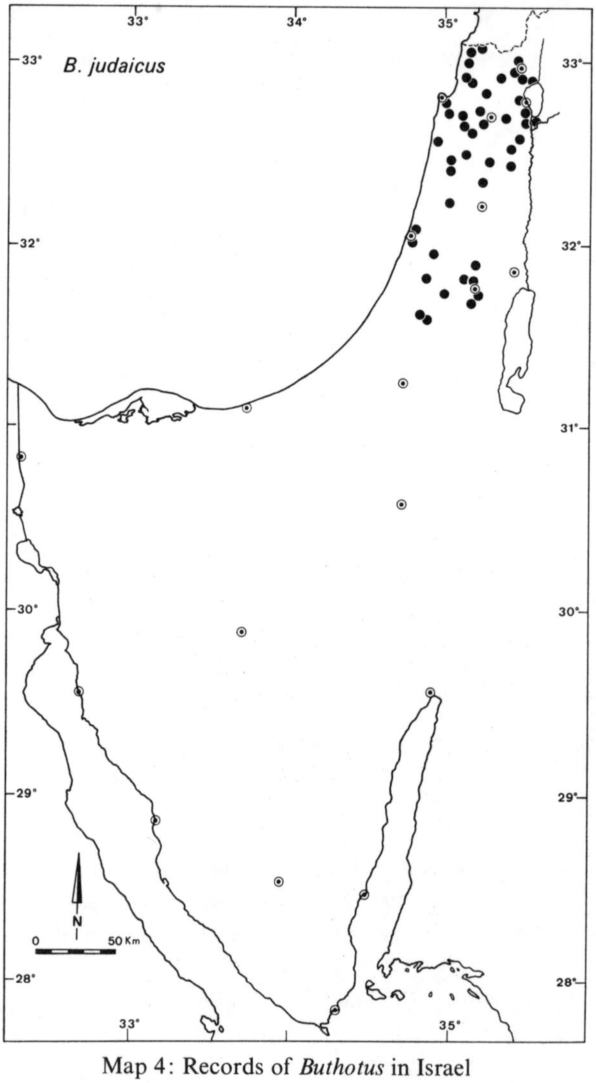

Map 4: Records of *Buthotus* in Israel

but apparently only following Werner (1902). The fact that it was not found again in Turkey is further confirmed by Vachon (1947a, 1947b, 1951) and Tolunay (1959). Syria: All authors, since Simon (1872), generally indicate the occurrence of *B. judaicus* in Syria, but no localities have been published. In just a few cases Palestine is given in parentheses after Syria. In fact, all the localities recorded by Simon (1872, 1892) are in Israel. The references of the following records are summarized in the Appendix on Distribution. Lebanon: Beirut; new record from the Muséum National, Paris (Dahr el Ain); the British Museum has specimens from Amiyun and the Hebrew University has specimens from Sin-el-fil and Kariye. Jordan: Jarash and its vicinity.

Israel (Map 4): *Buthotus judaicus* is found in Israel from the north to the Judean Mountains (Schenkel's 1932 record of Jericho for *B. judaicus* is no doubt incorrect). It also occurs along the Coastal Plain, from the north to the Tel Aviv area.

Ecological Notes: *Buthotus judaicus* is common in the Mediterranean zone of Israel. It is found on terra rossa, basalt, rendzina and brown-red sandy soils. The species occurs in zones with at least 350 to 400 mm annual rainfall. It lives under the bark of trees, small and large stones and in loosely built stone walls, and often enters houses. Parturition usually in July–August; number of young 15–18. It preys on small and large insects. The sting is painful but has no aftereffects.

Genus COMPSOBUTHUS Vachon, 1949

Archs Inst. Pasteur Algér., 27(1): 93

Type Species: *Buthus acutecarinatus* Simon, 1882.

Diagnosis: Prosoma with median-central and median-posterior crests united and forming a straight continuous line; tergites with three crests tapering posteriorly and projecting beyond posterior margin; latero-ventral crests of fifth segment almost smooth or with regular small granules.

Prosoma: Usually granulate with at least partly granulate crests; median-posterior crests ending behind posterior margin of prosoma in short points; latero-central crests separated from median-posterior crests; latero-posterior crests absent; posterior margin of prosoma concave in the middle between posterior projections of median-posterior crests; median eyes equidistant or separated from each other by more than their diameter.

Mesosoma: Tergites at least partly granulate, with three crests from first segment onwards.

Metasoma: Slender, anterior segments concave dorsally, fifth segment slightly convex; intermediary crests present or absent; segments 1–4 with distinct dorsal granulate crests; lateral anal lobes of fifth segment not projecting, vesicule rugose ventrally, with or without subaculear tubercle of varying size.

Pectines: Inner fulcra with short sclerotized point.

Pedipalps: Crests of tibia distinct; hand with or almost without crests; fingers with or without accessory denticles near all series of denticles; always four denticles, sometimes arranged in pairs under apical tooth of movable finger; fingers with or without recess and hump of varying size at base.
Walking Legs: Outer tooth of basitarsal spur simple, with only a few bristles; basitarsus without dorsal comb of bristles; sole of tarsi with bristles or hairs.

Review of Genus: the genus *Compsobuthus* consists mainly of species which were formerly considered to be subspecies of *Buthus acutecarinatus* (Simon). They are usually small species, less than 5 cm long, many only 2–3 cm. Some of them, although common, were not collected due to their small size. The genus has a wide distribution from Mauritania to Egypt, Ethiopia and Somalia, throughout the Middle East to Turkey and Iran in the north and to India in the east.
The presence or absence of a complement of outer accessory denticles on the movable finger of the pedipalp distinguishes two groups of this genus. However, the definite position of some specimens from India, Ethiopia, Turkey (all without outer denticles) and Iraq (with outer denticles), which doubtless belong to this genus, is still uncertain. *Compsobuthus matthiesseni,* which is included here provisionally, may belong to a different genus.

Without outer denticles (acutecarinatus group)	
Compsobuthus acutecarinatus (Simon, 1882)	Yemen, Aden, Hadhramaut
Compsobuthus maindroni (Kraepelin, 1900)	Muscat, Aden, Yemen, Somalia, Sudan (Red Sea coast)
Compsobuthus berlandi Vachon, 1950	Mauritania (?Algeria)
Compsobuthus jordanensis Levy, Amitai & Shulov, 1973	Jordan, Syrian Desert
Compsobuthus arabicus Levy, Amitai & Shulov, 1973	South Arabian Desert
?*Compsobuthus matthiesseni* (Birula, 1905)	Iraq, Iran
With outer denticles (werneri group)	
Compsobuthus rugosulus (Pocock, 1900)	India (?Afghanistan), Iran
Compsobuthus werneri werneri (Birula, 1908) [= ?*C. abyssinicus* (Birula, 1903 b)]	Sahara, Egypt, Sudan, Arabia, Sinai, southern Israel
Compsobuthus werneri judaicus (Birula, 1905) (= *C. schmiedeknechti* Vachon, 1949)	Central and northern Israel, Lebanon
Compsobuthus klaptoczi (Birula, 1909)	Libya
Compsobuthus manzoni (Borelli, 1915) [= *C. brevimanus* (Werner, 1936)]	Yemen
Compsobuthus carmelitis Levy, Amitai & Shulov, 1973	Israel (Mt. Carmel, Western and Lower Galilee;
Compsobuthus longipalpis Levy, Amitai & Shulov, 1973	Israel, Sinai (Jordan Rift)

Key to the Species of Compsobuthus in Israel and Sinai
(Map 5)

1. Segments of metasoma with numerous bristles ventrally, also between ventral crests 2
– Segments of metasoma with the usual number of bristles ventrally, without bristles between ventral crests (at most one or two hairs on anterior segments) 3

2. Intermediary crests of second segment of metasoma complete. **C. werneri werneri**
– Intermediary crests of second segment of metasoma with only 1–3 granules. **C. longipalpis**

3. Intermediary crests of third and fourth segments of metasoma complete. **C. werneri judaicus**
– Intermediary crests of third segment of metasoma with only 1–3 granules, fourth segment without intermediary crests. **C. carmelitis**

Compsobuthus werneri (Birula, 1908)

Buthus acutecarinatus werneri Birula, 1908, *Sber. Akad. Wiss. Wien,* 117 : 129–132. Type Locality: Wadi Halfa, northern Nubia, Sudan.
Compsobuthus werneri—. Vachon, 1949, *Archs Inst. Pasteur Algér.*, 27(1) : 97–100.

Prosoma: Median-ocular crests granulate throughout, extending to anterior margin; median-central crests behind median eyes curved inwards anteriorly.
Mesosoma: Sternites of segments 3–5 without crests, at most lateral crests of fifth sternite slightly indicated; sixth sternite with four crests which are sometimes indistinct; seventh sternite shagreened or with fine granulation laterally.
Metasoma: Segments 1 and 2 with 10 crests; intermediary crests of third segment complete and distinct, or only indicated and not extending over whole segment; fourth segment with or without completely granulate intermediary crests; dorsal crests of segments 1–4 distinct, ending with a large granule; segments 1–4 with little-marked dorsal accessory crests between dorsal crests, these more distinct on fourth segment; segments of metasoma with coarse or small granules dorsally; sides of segments granulate or shagreened, most densely on fifth segment; aculeus shorter than vesicule including pedicel but longer than or as wide as width of vesicule; subaculear tubercle of varying size; segments with the usual number or even numerous bristles ventrally, also between ventral crests; fifth segment with a latero-basal series of four bristles; anal margin of fifth segment with 4–6 bristles ventrally; stinger with bristles ventrally, mainly near pedicel.
Pectines: Outer side with short hairs; females with 12–21 denticles, males with 15–23 denticles.
Pedipalps: Femur shagreened or granulate; tibia shagreened or with small granules, with or without a few accessory short bristles on outer side; tibia wider than femur; hand slightly shagreened, distinctly shagreened or slightly granulate on inner side; dorsal and ventral crests present, median and intermediary crests distinct, indistinct or absent; hand narrower than tibia in females, hand as wide as tibia or slightly wider in males; movable finger with 9–10 series of denticles and outer accessory

denticles; finger of male sometimes with a small recess at base; fingers of females usually longer than those of males and distinctly more than twice as long as hand; fingers usually less than twice as long as hand in males; fingers longer than or as long as prosoma in both sexes.

Walking Legs: Coxae almost smooth or slightly shagreened, with crests in the form of raised lines or with granules on anterior margin; outer tooth of basitarsal spur of leg III with one hair; sole of tarsi with short hairs usually in two rows; legs granulate dorsally, lateral margin with raised lines or slightly serrate crests.

Systematic Remarks: Birula (1908) stated that *C. werneri* occurs in Lower and Upper Egypt and (1917) also in Eritrea and Somalia. Birula (1903b) had described another dark subspecies from Ethiopia, *Buthus acutecarinatus abyssinicus.* Birula (1908) also described a third subspecies from the Sudan (Khartum); however, he (1927) synonymized the latter with *abyssinicus.* Material from the Sudan to Lake Rudolf clearly belongs to *werneri.* There are dark specimens from Ethiopia in the Muséum National, Paris, without outer accessory denticles on the movable finger. Since Birula always mentioned these denticles in *abyssinicus*, these dark Ethiopian specimens may belong to another species.

Vachon (1949) recorded *werneri* from the Sahara. It also occurs in southern Arabia and Aden, as well as in Sinai, Israel and Lebanon. The species apparently has a very wide distribution. The form in central and northern Israel and in the Lebanon should be considered a separate subspecies of *C. werneri.*

Birula (1905) described *Buthus acutecarinatus judaicus* from (?)southern Palestine and Arabia-Petraea. He gave (1910) Jerusalem as the locality where this subspecies actually occurs. He also mentioned a very unusual character: the outer accessory denticles of the movable finger are arranged, at least in the distal part, in two rows. This is very surprising, as we have examined many hundreds of specimens, and all without exception have only one row of outer denticles. There are several possible explanations: (1) such a form indeed exists, but has not been found again; (2) Birula had a specimen with abnormal denticles on the fingers; (3) a mistake was made in the key for determination. This is most likely, as a similar mistake has been made with regard to *C. matthiesseni.*

Birula (1905, p. 140, key) stated that this species had outer denticles, but in the description (p. 143) he writes that it lacks these denticles. It is clear, however, from Birula's (1908) comparison of *judaicus* with the Egyptian *werneri* that he had before him the subspecies from the northern parts of Israel. Vachon (1949) mentioned this subspecies briefly, but considered it a different species, *C. schmiedeknechti.* Specimens from Nazareth in the Muséum National were labeled with this name by Kraepelin, but he apparently never published it.

Compsobuthus werneri werneri (Birula, 1908)

Figs. 57–61; Map 5

Description based on specimens from southern Israel and Sinai.
Coloration: Yellow to light yellow; crests on body and part of fifth segment of metasoma dark yellow. *Size*: Adult females are about 4 cm long or slightly longer.
Prosoma: With small granules; median eyes separated from each other by more than their diameter in females, and by the diameter of one median eye in males.
Mesosoma: Tergites with fine granulation which is denser laterally; seventh sternite shagreened laterally.
Metasoma: Intermediary crests of third segment indistinct, missing altogether on anterior part of segment; fourth segment without intermediary crests (at most with an indistinct line); fifth segment more than twice as long as wide or high; segments of metasoma dorsally with fine granulation, shagreened laterally; aculeus as long as

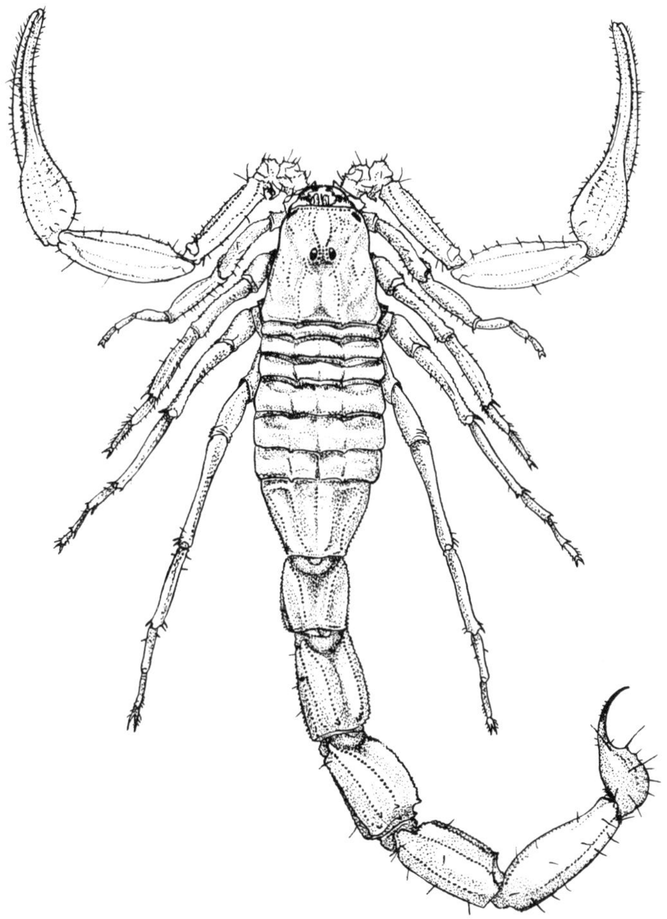

Fig. 57: *Compsobuthus werneri werneri* (Birula, 1908)
Male from Bir Zerer (108/105), Sinai (Sc. 2069); total length 30 mm

58

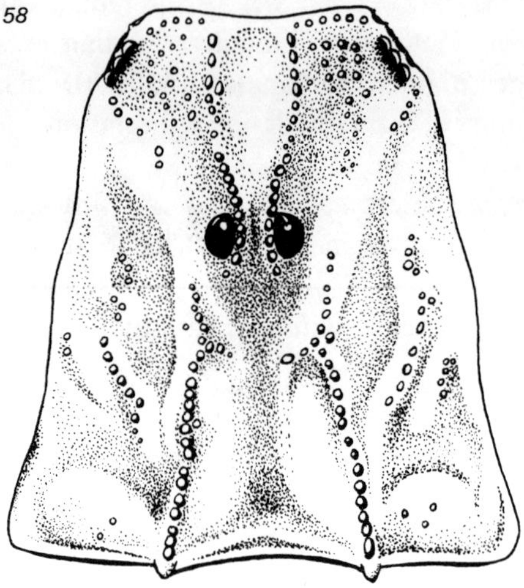

59

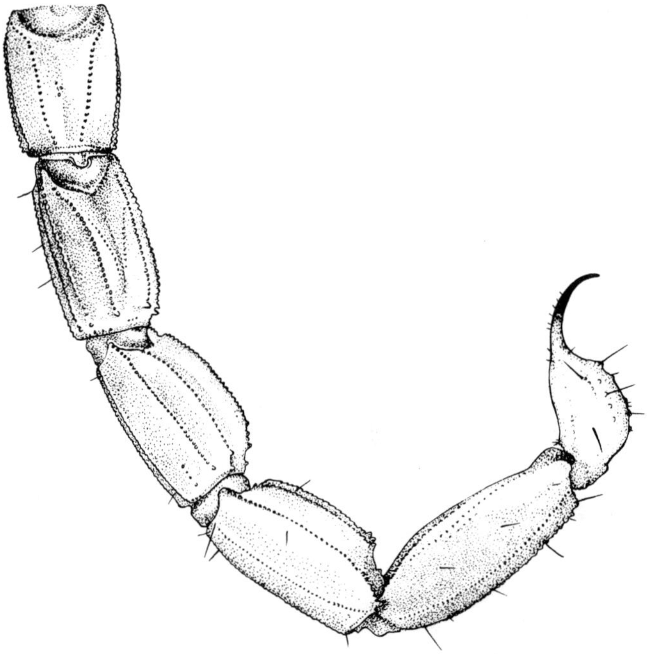

Figs. 58–59: *Compsobuthus werneri werneri* (Birula, 1908). 58. prosoma, length 3.5 mm; 59. metasoma, length 20 mm

60

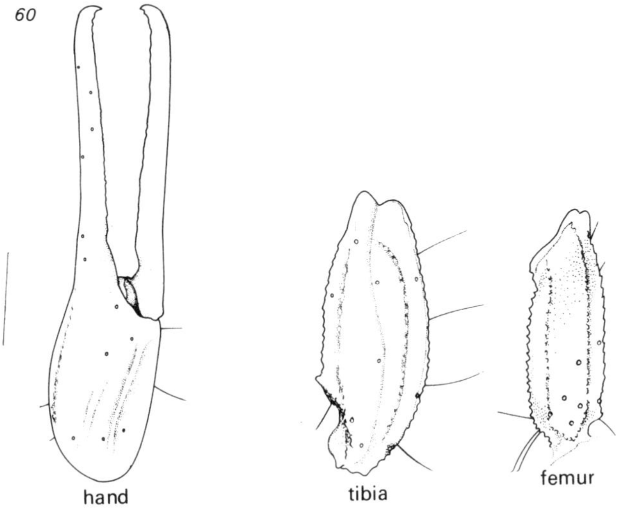

61

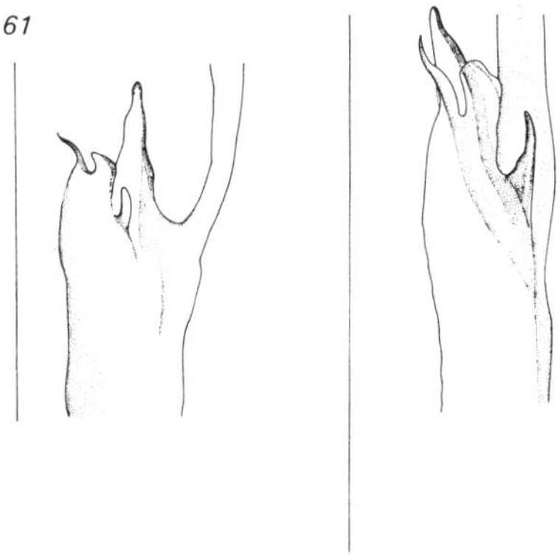

Figs. 60–61: *Compsobuthus werneri werneri* (Birula, 1908).
60. pedipalp, arrangement of trichobothria; 61. paraxial organ, form of lobes at base of flagellum; scale-lines 1 mm

vesicule without the pedicel* or slightly longer or shorter; segments of metasoma ventrally with numerous bristles, also between ventral crests.**
Pectines: Females with 16–21 (usually 17–19) denticles, males with 18–23 (usually 20–22) denticles.
Pedipalps: Femur and tibia shagreened; hand distinctly shagreened on inner side; median and intermediary crests absent (at most indistinct in females); movable finger with 10 series of denticles.

* Measurement of the length of the vesicule without the pedicel in this genus is from the base of the aculeus (= *soies aiguillonaires* of Vachon) to the dorsal saddle on the basal part of the vesicule.

** This relatively dense pilosity is not very marked in specimens from Egypt and the Sahara, but is present in specimens from the Sudan. Because of this slight difference, the distinction of our subspecies from *C. w. werneri* seems unjustified.

Measurements (mm): *Female*. Adult, Naḫal Mishmar, Judean Desert (No. Sc. 814). Total length 35; prosoma 3.7, mesosoma 10, metasoma 21. Segments of metasoma: first L2.0, W2.2, H1.9; second 2.6–2.0–1.9; third 2.7–1.9–1.9; fourth 3.0–1.8–1.8; fifth 3.9–1.8–1.8. Vesicule (without pedicel) L1.5, W1.3; pedicel L0.7, W0.8; aculeus L1.6. Pedipalps: femur L3.2, W1.0; tibia L4.0, W1.7; hand L2.2, W1.4; movable finger L4.8. Number of denticles of pectine 18–19.

Male. Adult, Naḫal Tamar, Judean Desert (No. Sc. 813). Total length 29; prosoma 3.3, mesosoma 7.0, metasoma 19. Segments of metasoma: first L2.0, W2.1, H1.9; second 2.5–1.9–1.9; third 2.7–1.9–1.9; fourth 3.0–1.8–1.8; fifth 3.6–1.7–1.7. Vesicule (without pedicel) L1.5. W1.3; pedicel L0.6, W0.8; aculeus L1.6. Pedipalps: femur L3.0, W0.9; tibia L3.7, W1.4; hand L2.1, W1.6; movable finger L4.4. Number of denticles of pectine 22–22.

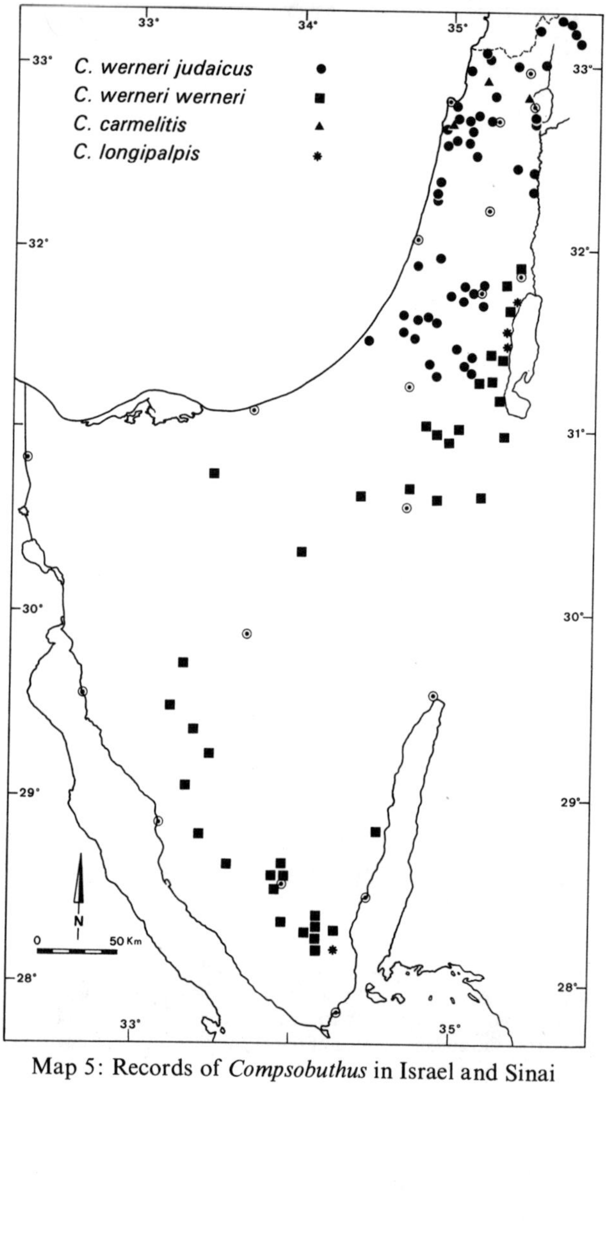

Map 5: Records of *Compsobuthus* in Israel and Sinai

Distribution: Northern Africa. Arabia: records from the British Museum: South Arabia, Aden.
Israel and Sinai (Map 5): No species of *Compsobuthus* has previously been recorded from southern Israel and Sinai. *Compsobuthus werneri werneri* is found in southern and central Sinai. It probably also occurs in northern Sinai, but is absent in the coastal zone. In Israel it is distributed throughout the south, extending north along the Judean Desert to Jericho.
Ecological Notes: *Compsobuthus werneri werneri* is fairly common. It is found on brown desert soils and in stony desert. It lives in rock crevices and fissures in the soil and under small stones. It often clings upside down to the underside of a stone. It usually occurs singly; in rare cases two or three specimens are found together. The metasoma is characteristically curved laterally. It does not sting readily. Parturition usually in May–June; number of young 5–14. It preys on small arthropods and avoids insects even half its size.

Compsobuthus werneri judaicus (Birula, 1905)

Figs. 62–64; Map 5

Buthus acutecarinatus judaicus Birula, 1905, *Bull. Acad. Imp. Sci. St.-Pétersbourg,* (5)23(1–2): 140. Type Locality: Jerusalem.
Compsobuthus schmiedeknechti Vachon, 1949, *Archs Inst. Pasteur Algér.,* 27(1): 99. Type Locality: Nazareth; type deposited in the Muséum National, Paris; examined.

Coloration: Dark brown to light yellow. Crests on body and part of fifth segment of metasoma darker than other parts in light specimens. *Size*: Adults less than 3 cm long; only a few females are 3 cm or slightly longer.
Prosoma: Densely and coarsely granulate; median eyes separated from each other by more than their diameter in both sexes.
Mesosoma: Tergites granulate, granules coarser and more numerous laterally; seventh sternite with fine granulation laterally.
Metasoma: Segments 3 and 4 with complete, distinct intermediary crests; fifth segment less than twice as long as wide or high; segments with dense, coarse granules dorsally, granules less coarse laterally; aculeus distinctly shorter than vesicule without pedicel, rarely of the same length; segments with the usual number of bristles ventrally, without bristles between ventral crests.
Pectines: Females with 12–16 (usually 13–15) denticles, males with 15–18 (usually 16–17) denticles.
Pedipalps: Femur and tibia with fine granulation; hand slightly granulate on inner side; median and intermediary crests distinct or indistinct; movable finger with nine series of denticles.
Measurements (mm): *Female.* Adult, Jerusalem (No. Sc. 1374). Total length 29; prosoma 3.3, mesosoma 8.7, metasoma 17. Segments of metasoma: first L1.7, W2.0, H1.7; second 2.0–1.8–1.7; third 2.2–1.7–1.7; fourth 2.5–1.6–1.6; fifth 3.0–1.6–1.5. Vesicule (without pedicel) L1.5, W1.2; pedicel L0.5, W0.7; aculeus L1.4. Pedipalps:

femur L2.6, W0.9; tibia L3.2, W1.2; hand L1.7, W1.1; movable finger L3.5. Number of denticles of pectine 14–14.

Male. Adult, Kefar HaḤoresh (No. Sc. 1378). Total length 24; prosoma 3.0, mesosoma 6.0, metasoma 15. Segments of metasoma: first L1.5, W1.9, H1.7; second 1.8–1.8–1.7; third 2.1–1.8–1.7; fourth 2.3–1.7–1.7; fifth 2.9–1.6–1.5. Vesicule (without pedicel) L1.4, W1.2; pedicel L0.4, W0.7; aculeus L1.2. Pedipalps: femur L2.4, W0.8; tibia L2.9, W1.1; hand L1.7, W1.2; movable finger L3.1. Number of denticles of pectine 15–16.

Distribution: The references of the following records are summarized in the Appendix on Distribution. Lebanon: The Muséum National, Paris, has a female from Ba'albek — *leg*. Kerville, 1911, wrongly identified by Simon as *B. gibbosus*.

Israel (Map 5; p. 66): *Compsobuthus w. judaicus* occurs in Israel from the north to the southern foothills of Judea, as well as along the Coastal Plain to the Gaza area.

Ecological Notes: *Compsobuthus werneri judaicus* is very common. It is found on various types of soil: terra rossa, basalt, rendzina, brown-red sandy soils and, to a lesser extent, on loess. It lives in rock and soil crevices, under the tree bark and under small and large stones. Aggregations of over twenty specimens of both sexes are sometimes found under the same stone in winter (Zinner & Amitai, 1969). It does not sting readily and can be kept in large numbers in containers without cannibalism. Parturition usually in May–June; number of young 5–12. It preys on small arthropods. Like *C. w. werneri*, it often clings to the underside of a stone and the metasoma is usually curved laterally.

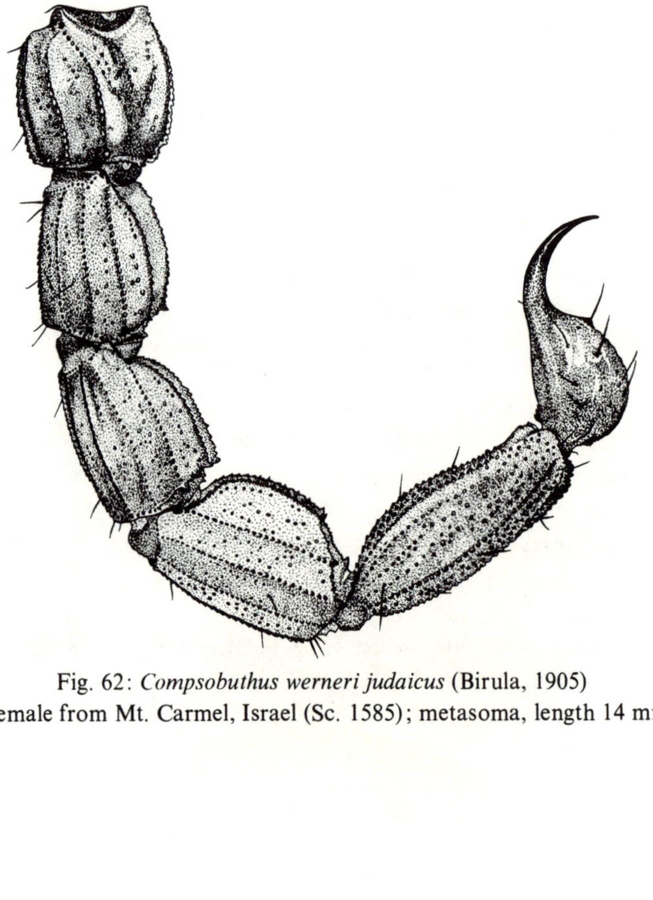

Fig. 62: *Compsobuthus werneri judaicus* (Birula, 1905)
Female from Mt. Carmel, Israel (Sc. 1585); metasoma, length 14 mm

63

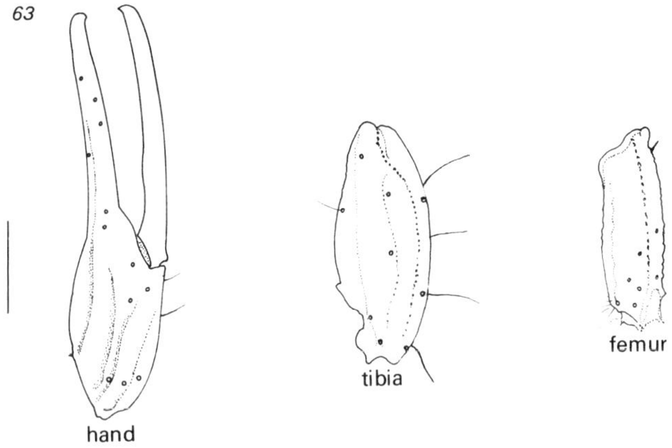

64

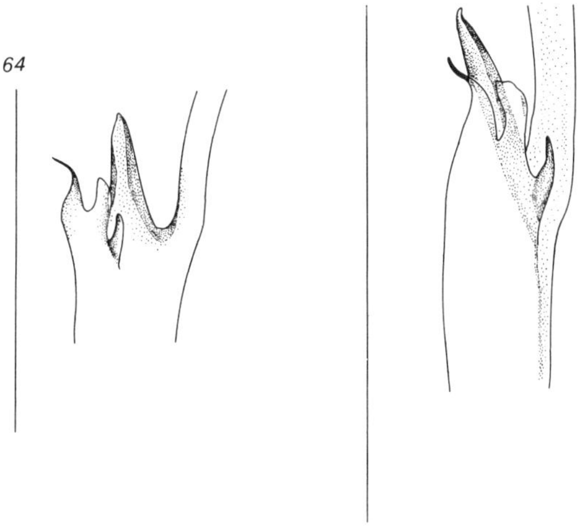

Figs. 63–64: *Compsobuthus werneri judaicus* (Birula, 1905)
63. pedipalp, arrangement of trichobothria;
64. paraxial organ, form of lobes at base of flagellum; scale-lines 1 mm

Systematic Remarks: More than 300 specimens were examined: about 200 of the northern *C. w. judaicus* and 100 of the southern *C. w. werneri*. The main distinguishing characters between the two subspecies are: the intermediary crests on segments 3 and 4 of the metasoma; the number of series of denticles on the movable finger; the density of the bristles and intensity of granulation; the number of denticles on the pectine.

The southern specimens are usually larger than the northern. In *C. w. judaicus,* females are 21–32 mm and males 20–29 mm long. In *C. w. werneri,* females are 29–39 mm and males 27–31 mm long. The appendages of the southern forms are also longer and thicker. In *C. w. judaicus* the width of the hand is 1.1 mm in both sexes and the length of the hand plus the length of the movable finger is 4.5 mm in males and 5.1 mm in females (average). The equivalent measurements for *C. w.*

werneri are: width of hand 1.4 mm in both sexes, length of hand plus finger 6.1 mm in males and 7.0 mm in females.

The border between the range of the two subspecies in Israel more or less follows the line of 350 mm average annual rainfall, which is parallel to the southern border of the Mediterranean flora. At least in one area, along the northern parts of the Dead Sea shore (Duyūk, Jericho, Ma'ale Adummim, 'En Fashkha, 'En et Turaba), an intermediate population with mixed characters of both subspecies has been found. The characters of the southern *C. w. werneri* are relatively dominant over those of the northern subspecies in this population. The size, number of denticles on the pectine, number of series of denticles on the movable finger, incomplete intermediary crests on the third segment of the metasoma and fine granulation of the body are all significant characters of the southern subspecies. On the other hand, all forms have (though sometimes only slightly marked) intermediary crests on the fourth segment of the metasoma, number of bristles on metasoma reduced, i.e. bristles between ventral crests absent, rarely one or two bristles on one segment. These are characters of *C. w. judaicus*. However, at the southernmost point of this interbreeding zone, 'En et Turaba, specimens were found which are clearly *C. w. werneri,* without any characters of *C. w. judaicus*. Since the southern characters are predominant in this population, the specimens were included in the range of *C. w. werneri*.

The existence of an intermediate population and the close morphological resemblance suggest that these are subspecies, not species.

Compsobuthus carmelitis Levy, Amitai & Shulov, 1973

Figs. 65–67; Map 5

Zool. J. Linn. Soc. Lond., 52:115. Type Locality: Mt. Carmel; type (female, No. Sc. 861) deposited in the Hebrew University, Jerusalem.

Coloration: Body, pedipalps and legs light yellow to light brownish yellow; crests on prosoma yellow or dark; fifth segment of metasoma slightly darker on anterior part of segment. *Size*: Females may be 4 cm long or longer.

Prosoma: Shagreened in the middle and with fine granulation anteriorly between median-ocular crests and lateral eyes, as well as on posterior and lateral parts; median-ocular crests granulate throughout; median eyes separated from each other by slightly more than their diameter in females and by the diameter of one median eye in males.

Mesosoma: Tergites with small granules; sternites 3–5 without crests; sixth sternite with four crests, lateral pair of crests with small granules, inner pair smooth; seventh sternite slightly shagreened.

Metasoma: Second segment with eight complete crests and two indistinct intermediary crests extending posteriorly only for one third or half of the segment; intermediary crests of third segment with only 1–3 granules on posterior part of segment; fourth segment without intermediary crests; dorsal crests of segments 1–4 distinct, granule at the end almost as large as the others; segments 1–4 with

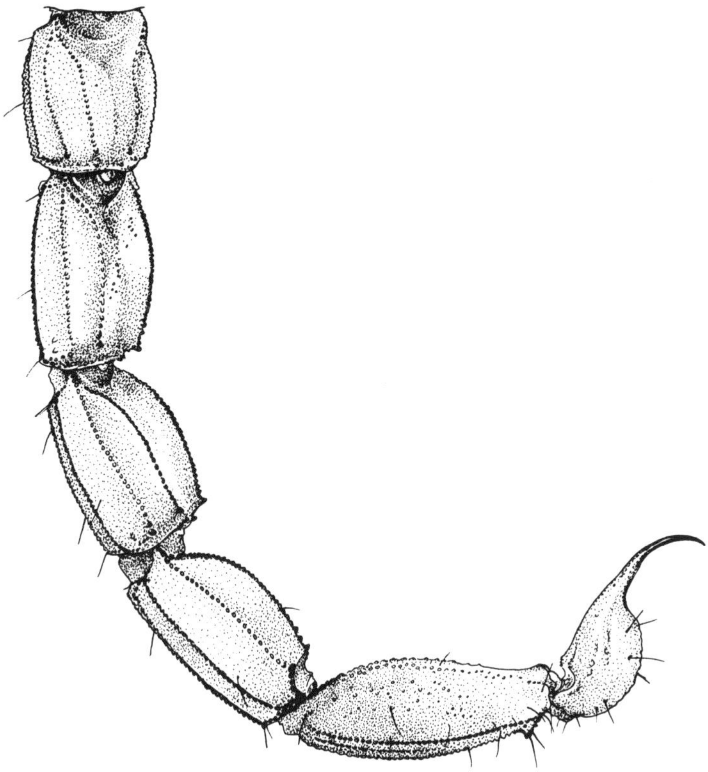

Fig. 65: *Compsobuthus carmelitis* Levy, Amitai & Shulov, 1973
Male from Mt. Carmel, Israel (Sc. 860); metasoma, length 21 mm

slightly marked dorsal-accessory crests between dorsal crests, these more distinct on fourth segment; segments shagreened dorsally and with small granules; sides of segments slightly shagreened, with small granules only at sides of fifth segment; fifth segment distinctly more than twice as long as wide or high; aculeus shorter than vesicule including pedicel, but distinctly longer than vesicule without pedicel; aculeus distinctly longer than width of vesicule; subaculear tubercle absent or only slightly indicated; segments with the usual number of bristles, without bristles between ventral crests; fifth segment with a latero-basal series of about four bristles.
Pectines: Extending beyond coxo-trochanteral articulation of leg IV in both sexes; outer side with short hairs; females with 20–22 denticles, males with 23–25 denticles.
Pedipalps: Femur and tibia long and slender, shagreened and without outer accessory bristles; tibia wider than femur; hand slightly shagreened on all sides, only dorsal crests slightly marked, almost absent; hand slightly wider than tibia in both sexes; movable finger with 12 series of denticles, outer accessory denticles near all series; fingers of male only with a shallow recess at base; movable finger of female longer than that of male, distinctly more than twice as long as hand; finger twice as long as hand in male; fingers distinctly longer than prosoma in both sexes.

66

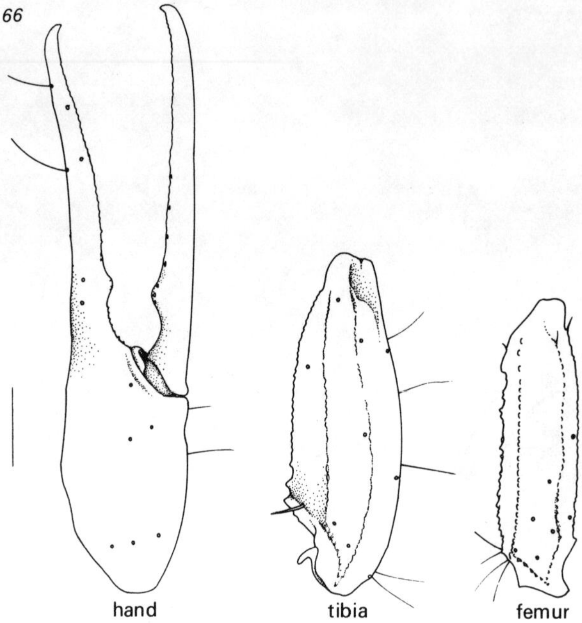

67

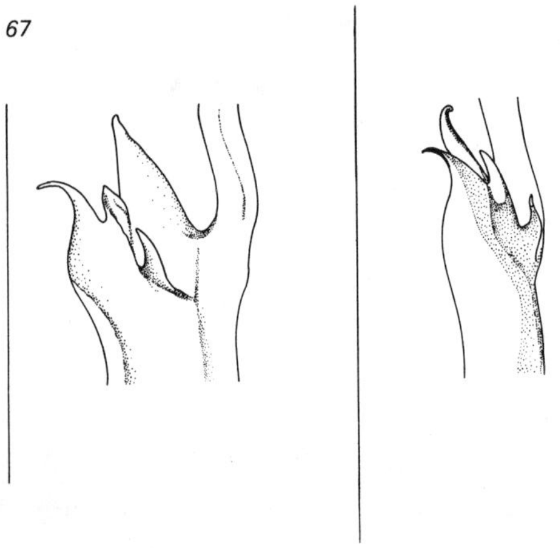

Figs. 66–67: *Compsobuthus carmelitis* Levy, Amitai & Shulov, 1973
66. pedipalp, arrangement of trichobothria; 67. paraxial organ, form of lobes at base of flagellum; scale-lines 1 mm

Walking Legs: Coxae slightly shagreened, anterior margin with granulate crests; outer tooth of basitarsal spur of leg III with one hair; sole of tarsi with short hairs in two rows; legs slightly shagreened dorsally, lateral margin of proximal segments with low crests.

Measurements (mm): *Female*. Adult, Naẖal Me'arot, Mt. Carmel (No. Sc. 861). Total length 39; prosoma 4.5, mesosoma 10, metasoma 24.5. Segments of metasoma:

first L2.4, W2.5, H2.1; second 3.0–2.2–2.1; third 3.2–2.1–2.1; fourth 3.6–2.0–2.1; fifth 4.4–1.9–1.9. Vesicule (without pedicel) L1.6, W1.6; pedicel L0.8, W1.0; aculeus L2.0. Pedipalps: femur L4.2, W1.2; tibia L5.1, W1.7; hand L2.7, W1.8; movable finger L6.1. Number of denticles of pectine 20–20.

Male. Adult, Naẖal Me'arot, Mt. Carmel (No. Sc. 860). Total length 32.6; prosoma 3.6, mesosoma 8.0, metasoma 21. Segments of metasoma: first L2.0, W2.1, H1.9; second 2.7–2.0–1.9; third 2.8–1.9–1.9; fourth 3.1–1.8–1.9; fifth 3.8–1.7–1.7. Vesicule (without pedicel) L1.4, W1.4; pedicel L0.7, W0.8; aculeus L1.6. Pedipalps: femur L3.6, W1.0; tibia L4.5, W1.5; hand L2.5, W1.7; movable finger L5.0. Number of denticles of pectine 24–25.

Distribution, Israel (Map 5; p. 66): Records of *C. carmelitis* are from only a few localities in the western Upper Galilee, Mount Carmel, and from Arbel in the eastern Lower Galilee.

Ecological Notes: *Compsobuthus carmelitis* is very rare. It is found on terra rossa, probably in slightly humid localities. It lives under stones. Parturition in July; about twelve young.

Compsobuthus longipalpis Levy, Amitai & Shulov, 1973

Figs. 68–69; Map 5

Zool. J. Linn. Soc. Lond., 52: 117. Type Locality: Naẖal 'Arugot, near 'En Gedi, Israel; type (subadult male, No. Sc. 1266) deposited in the Hebrew University, Jerusalem.

The following description is based on a few almost adult specimens, apparently males.

Coloration: Body, pedipalps and legs light yellow; crests on prosoma and tergites may be dark; two thirds of anterior part of fifth segment of metasoma black. *Size*: Length 4.0–5.0 cm.

Prosoma: Smooth, except for a few small granules anteriorly between median-ocular crests and lateral eyes and on posterior and lateral parts; median-ocular crests not extending to anterior margin.

Mesosoma: Tergites smooth between crests, but slightly granulate laterally; posterior margin of tergites with short hairs; sternites 3 to 6 smooth, without crests, at most with slightly indicated smooth lateral crests on sixth sternite; seventh sternite smooth, with four slightly indicated crests, inner pair smooth, lateral pair slightly serrate.

Metasoma: Second segment with eight complete and two intermediary crests with only 1–3 granules in posterior part of segment; intermediary crests of third segment with only 1–2 granules in posterior part of segment; fourth segment without intermediary crests; dorsal crests of segments 1–4 distinct, ending with a granule not larger than the others; dorsal accessory crests absent; latero-ventral crests smooth, at most fused granules on posterior segments; sides of all segments smooth; fifth segment distinctly more than 2.5 times longer than wide or high; aculeus shorter than vesicule including pedicel but distinctly longer than vesicule without pedicel; aculeus distinctly longer than width of vesicule; segments with bristles ventrally, also between ventral crests; stinger with many bristles.

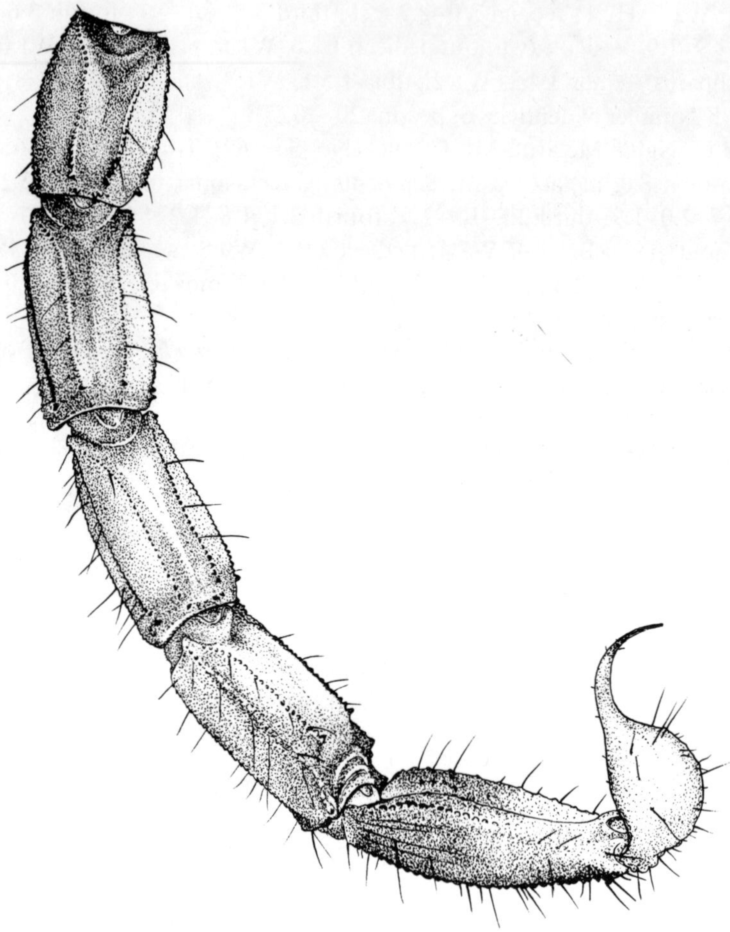

Fig. 68: *Compsobuthus longipalpis* Levy, Amitai & Shulov, 1973
Subadult male (?) from Naḫal 'Arugot, Israel (Sc. 1266); metasoma, length 24 mm

Pectines: Extending beyond coxo-trochanteral articulation of leg IV; outer side with short hairs; number of denticles of pectine 25–29 (apparently males).

Pedipalps: Femur and tibia very long, slender and smooth, without outer accessory bristles; tibia wider than femur; hand smooth on all sides and without crests, at most dorsal crests indicated, practically absent; hand very short, about as wide as tibia; movable finger with 14 series of denticles, with outer accessory denticles near all series; fingers very thin, about three times longer than hand, much longer than prosoma.

Walking Legs: Coxae smooth, their anterior margin with slightly granulate crests; outer tooth of basitarsal spur of leg III with one hair; sole of tarsi with short hairs in two rows; legs smooth dorsally.

Measurements (mm): ?*Male*. Subadult, Naḫal 'Arugot near 'En Gedi (No. Sc. 1266). Total length 43; prosoma 4.5, mesosoma 14.5, metasoma 24. Segments of metasoma:

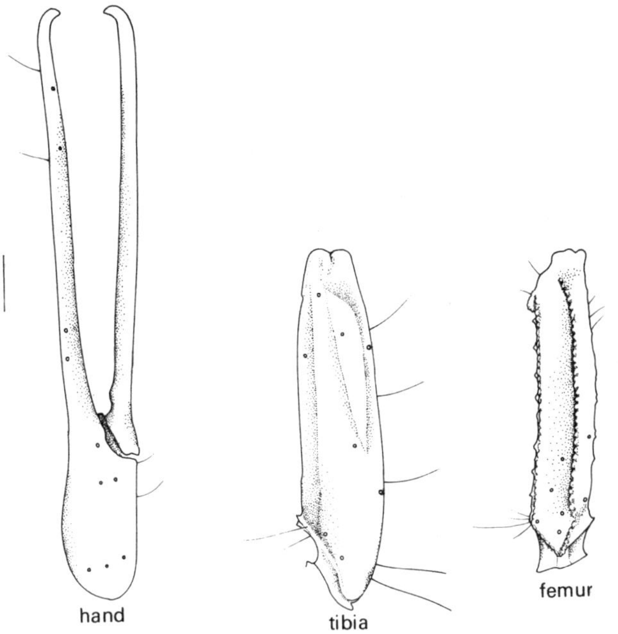

Fig. 69: *Compsobuthus longipalpis* Levy, Amitai & Shulov, 1973
Pedipalp, arrangement of trichobothria; scale-line 1 mm

first L2.7, W2.4, H2.1; second 3.3–2.2–2.0; third 3.4–2.1–2.0; fourth 3.8–1.9–1.8; fifth 4.4–1.7–1.7. Vesicule (without pedicel) L1.7, W1.5; pedicel L0.7, W1.0; aculeus damaged. Pedipalps: femur L4.9, W1.1; tibia L5.8, W1.6; hand L2.5, W1.4; movable finger L7.1. Number of denticles of pectine 28–28.

Distribution, Israel and Sinai (Map 5; p. 66): *Compsobuthus longipalpis* was found in just a few localities near the Dead Sea, and also in southeastern Sinai.

Ecological Notes: *Compsobuthus longipalpis* is very rare. It is found in alluvial desert soil. It lives under stones and probably also in rock crevices.

Genus BUTHACUS Birula, 1908

Sber. Akad. Wiss. Wien, 117(2;1): 139

Type Species: *Androctonus* (*Leiurus*) *leptochelys* Hemprich & Ehrenberg, 1829.

Diagnosis: Crests on prosoma usually absent or indistinct; fourth and fifth segments of metasoma without distinctly granulate dorsal crests.

Prosoma: Smooth or granulate.

Mesosoma: Tergites smooth or slightly granulate, sometimes only posterior tergites with three smooth or granulate crests; crests of seventh sternite smooth.

Metasoma: Slender, two posterior segments convex dorsally, without distinctly granulate dorsal crests; intermediary crests on second and third segments, rarely on

fourth; fifth segment usually with distinct lateral anal lobes; vesicule of stinger slender, without subaculear tubercle.
Pectines: Inner fulcra with or without fine hairs.
Pedipalps: Tibia without or with only slightly indicated crests; fingers with or without outer tooth near series of denticles; usually four denticles, rarely three, under apical tooth of movable finger.
Walking Legs: Outer tooth of basitarsal spur simple, with many bristles; basitarsi of three anterior legs always with a dorsal comb of bristles; sole of tarsi with long bristles or hairs.

Review of Genus: *Buthacus* has a wide distribution from Senegal and Morocco to Sudan and Somalia, and from Sinai and southern Israel to the Syrian Desert and Iraq in the north and to Arabia and eastern Iran in the east.
The presence or absence of a complement of outer accessory denticles on the movable finger of the pedipalp distinguishes the two groups of this genus. These groups could be further divided according to other characters, however, the definite position of several forms from North Africa is still uncertain.

A. With complete (or almost complete) set of outer denticles

1. *Species with usual pilosity on segments of metasoma*

Buthacus leptochelys leptochelys (Hemprich & Ehrenberg, 1829)	Syrian Desert, ?Iraq, ?southeastern Iran, ?Jordan, southern Israel, southern Sinai, Egypt, Chad, Niger, southern Libya, southern Algeria, ?Morocco
B. l. occidentalis Vachon, 1953	Mauritania
B. l. granosus (Borelli, 1929)	Sudan (Red Sea coast)
B. l. nitzani Levy, Amitai & Shulov, 1973	Southern Israel
Buthacus calviceps (Pocock, 1900 b)	Somalia
Buthacus foleyi Vachon, 1948	Southwestern Libya, southern Algeria
Buthacus villiersi Vachon, 1949	Senegal

2. *Species with dense pilosity on segments of metasoma*

Buthacus yotvatensis Levy, Amitai & Shulov, 1973	Israel ('Arava Valley), Syrian Desert, ?Iraq
B. y. nigroaculeatus Levy, Amitai & Shulov, 1973	Bahrain

B. Some or all outer denticles absent

1. *Slender forms, males with slender hands*

Buthacus arenicola (Simon, 1885)	Northern Sinai, Egypt (Suez Canal), western Libya, southern Tunisia

2. *Broad forms, males with broad hands*

Buthacus spatzi Birula, 1911	Central Tunisia; northeastern Algeria

Another three species may also belong to this genus: (1) *Androctonus (Leiurus) thebanus* Hemprich & Ehrenberg, 1829, from Egypt, cannot be identified with certainty; (2) *Buthus tadmorensis* Simon, 1892, described from Palmyra, Syrian Desert, is probably a synonym of *B. leptochelys,* since all pertinent specimens from Syria in Simon's collection belong to this species; (3) Werner (1936) described a dry specimen from Eritrea as *Buthacus frontalis.* This last specimen has not been re-examined, but according to the description it probably does not belong to *Buthacus.* Another species, *B. minipectenibus* Levy et al., 1973, from Arabia, may probably be placed in the genus *Vachoniolus* (Vachon, personal communication).

Key to the Species of Buthacus in Israel and Sinai
(Map 6)

1. Finger of pedipalp with outer accessory denticles near series of denticles (Fig. 8) 2
– Finger of pedipalp without outer denticles. **B. arenicola**
2. Segments of metasoma with the usual pilosity 3
– Segments of metasoma with dense rows of bristles along dorsal and latero-dorsal crests. **B. yotvatensis**
3. Intermediary crests of second segment of metasoma not extending to half of segment; latero-ventral crests of third segment of metasoma almost smooth in anterior part, but with small, almost usual teeth posteriorly. **B. leptochelys leptochelys**
– Intermediary crests of second segment of metasoma extending to about half of segment; latero-ventral crests of third segment of metasoma with distinct medium-sized teeth throughout. **B. leptochelys nitzani**

Buthacus leptochelys (Hemprich & Ehrenberg, 1829)

Androctonus (Leiurus) leptochelys Hemprich & Ehrenberg, 1829, *Berolini ex officina Academica*: 119. Type Locality: Sinai.
Androctonus (Leiurus) macrocentrus Hemprich & Ehrenberg, 1829, *Berolini ex officina Academica*: 119, pl. 1, fig. 6. Type Locality: Sinai.
Buthus leptochelys—. Kraepelin, 1891, *Jb. Hamb. Wiss. Anst.,* 8 : 60–62 (in part).
Buthus tadmorensis Simon, 1892, *Revue Biol. Nord. Fr. (Lille)*, 5 : 84. Type Locality: Palmyra, Syrian Desert.
Buthus (Buthacus) leptochelys—. Birula, 1908, *Sber. Akad. Wiss. Wien,* 117 : 139–141 (in part).
Buthacus leptochelys—. Simon, 1910, *Bull. Soc. Ent. Égypte*: 74–76 (in part).

Coloration: Uniformly yellow or partly reddish orange, mainly on anterior part of prosoma and fifth segment of metasoma. *Size*: Adults 4–6 cm long.
Prosoma: Median-ocular crests smooth or slightly granulate, distinct almost only near median eyes; median eyes situated anterior to middle.
Mesosoma: Crests of tergites almost absent or only slightly indicated, mainly on posterior segments; seventh sternite smooth; sternites with bristles mainly laterally and on posterior margin.
Metasoma: First segment with 10 crests; segments 2 and 3 with eight complete and two short intermediary crests; latero-ventral crests of third segment with serrate

denticles; fourth segment without intermediary crests, sometimes with one granule; latero-dorsal crests of segment 4 indistinct; axial and ventral crests of fifth segment distinct or indistinct; latero-ventral crests of fifth segment with irregular teeth of varying number and size; postero-ventral margin of segment 5 with 7–12 teeth and 2–3 lateral anal lobes; vesicule narrower than fifth segment; aculeus longer than vesicule including pedicel; segments 1–5 smooth, ventral side of posterior segments slightly shagreened; segments 1–4 with a row of bristles at posterior ventral margin; segments of metasoma with the usual number of bristles; fifth segment with a latero-basal row of up to 8 bristles, anal margin with 4–6 bristles and stinger with bristles ventrally, mainly near pedicel.

Pectines: Outer side with short hairs; females with 18–29 denticles, males with 27–35 denticles.

Pedipalps: Femur slightly granulate, inner side with a few bristles and outer side with short accessory bristles; tibia with one or a few bristles on inner side, without accessory bristles on outer side; hand smooth, without crests, wider or narrower than tibia in males; fingers with 8–10 series of denticles, outer accessory denticles present; four denticles under apical tooth of movable finger.

Walking Legs: Outer tooth of basitarsal spur large and with many bristles on legs III and IV; dorsal combs of basitarsi and tibiae with many bristles.

Systematic Remarks: Hemprich & Ehrenberg (1829) described *Androctonus* (*Leiurus*) *leptochelys* and *Androctonus* (*Leiurus*) *macrocentrus* from the same locality. These are now considered to be the two sexes of the same species, the first the male, the second the female.

Buthacus leptochelys has a wide distribution from Mauritania to the Sudan and from Sinai to the Syrian Desert, and it probably also occurs in Iraq and southeastern Iran. All these populations are at present considered to belong to the same species.

Borelli (1929) described *Buthacus granosus* (a male with 29–30 denticles on the pectine) from Port Sudan on the Red Sea. A female (24–27 denticles) from Duroor. north of Suakin (*leg.* Anderson, 1894) probably also belongs to this form. Examination of the type in the British Museum proved that *B. granosus* is a subspecies of *B. leptochelys*. Vachon (1953) described another subspecies, *B. l. occidentalis*, from Mauritania.

Buthacus l. leptochelys forms several widely separated populations in Sinai and Israel. A constant connection between these populations has not been found. One population was found in southern Sinai near the shore of the Red Sea, a second in Israel on the southern coast of the Mediterranean and a third, also in Israel, inland, near Mamshit. Another subspecies, *B. l. nitzani*, was recently found on inland sand dunes in southern Israel. It differs from *B. l. leptochelys* in its smaller size, broad hands, fewer denticles on the pectine and in the intermediary crests on the segments of the metasoma. Specimens of *B. leptochelys* were also found in eastern Jordan. However, these are very young and small, and their systematic position cannot be determined. There is new material from the Syrian Desert (Palmyra, 1965; RS–4335) in the Muséum National, Paris which apparently belongs to *B. l. leptochelys*; thus these juveniles from Jordan may possibly also be of the same subspecies.

Buthacus leptochelys leptochelys (Hemprich & Ehrenberg, 1829)
Figs. 70–74; Map 6

Coloration: Uniformly yellow. *Size*: Adults about 6 cm long.
Prosoma: Median eyes large, separated from each other by more than their diameter; lateral eyes small, combined length of all three lateral eyes only slightly exceeding the diameter of one median eye.
Mesosoma: Crests of tergites almost absent, only slightly indicated on posterior segments.

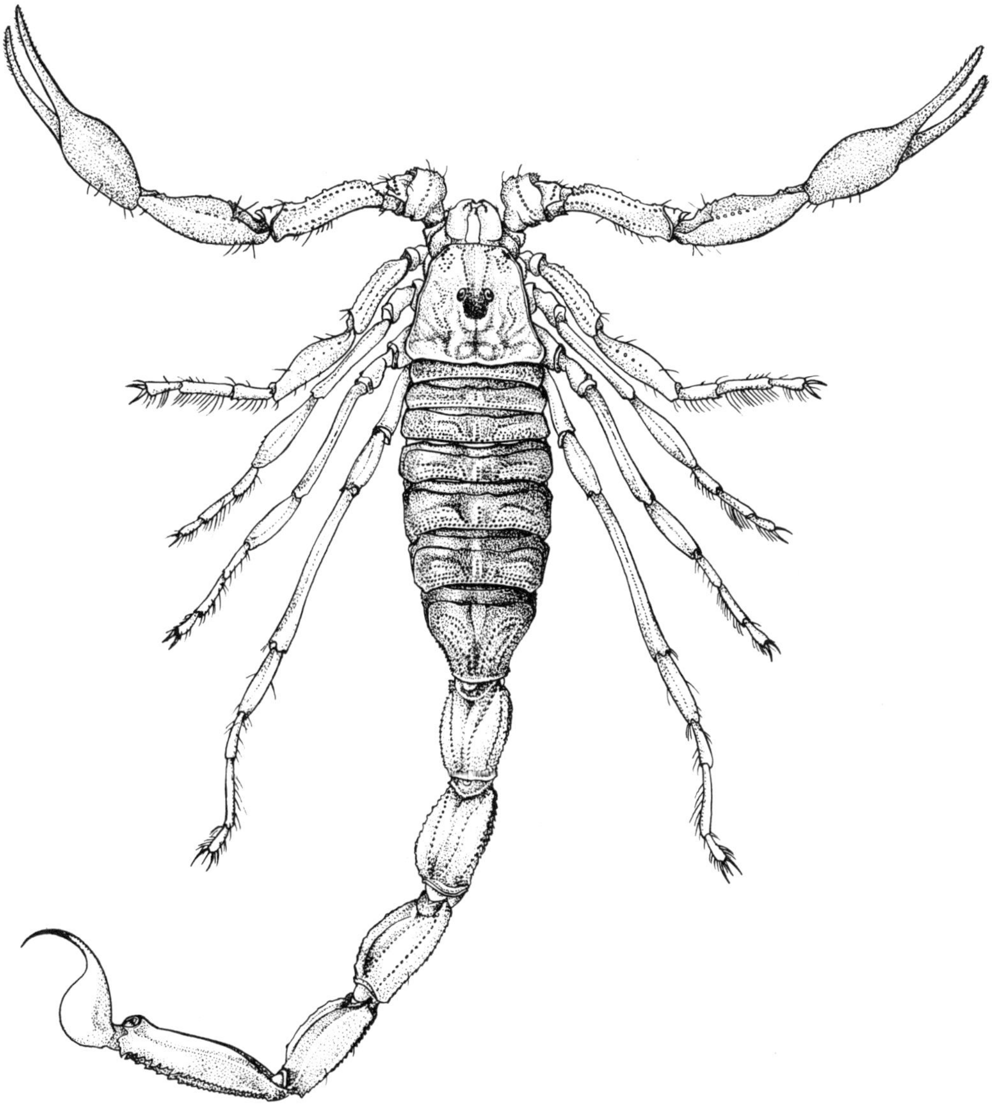

Fig. 70: *Buthacus leptochelys leptochelys* (Hemprich & Ehrenberg, 1829)
Male from Palmaḇim, Israel (Sc. 1513); total length 53 mm

71

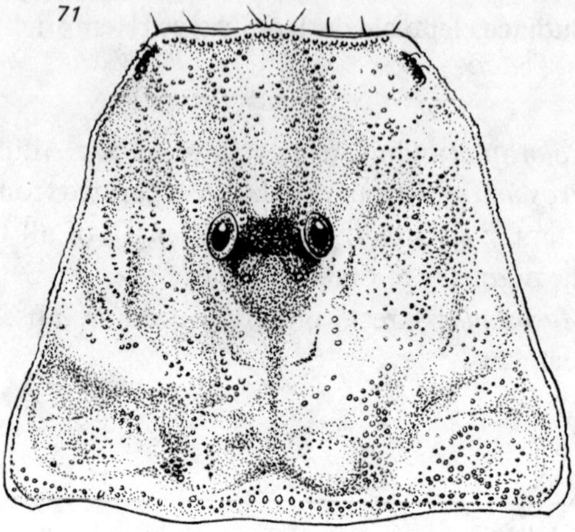

72

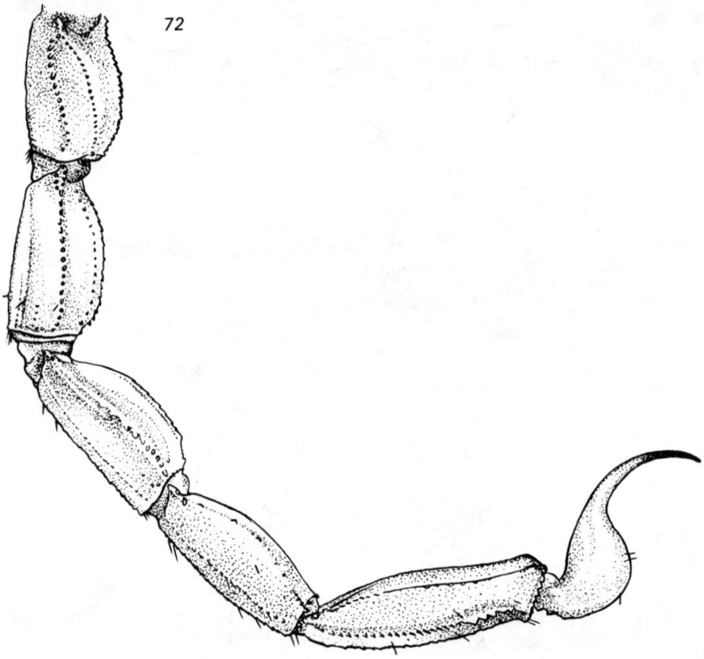

Figs. 71–72: *Buthacus leptochelys leptochelys* (Hemprich & Ehrenberg, 1829)
71. prosoma, length 5.0 mm; 72. metasoma, length 34 mm

Metasoma: Intermediary crests of second segment not extending to half of segment, with only 2–4 granules on third segment; latero-ventral crests of third segment smooth in anterior part but with small, almost regular teeth posteriorly which project slightly more in females than in males; ventral crests of fifth segment indistinct, and axial crests nearly absent, also in males; latero-ventral crests of fifth segment with irregular triangular teeth of varying size; lateral anal lobes distinct and larger than 9–12 small teeth on posterior ventral margin of fifth segment; vesicule smooth ventrally near pedicel; fourth and mainly fifth segment sometimes shagreened ventrally.

73

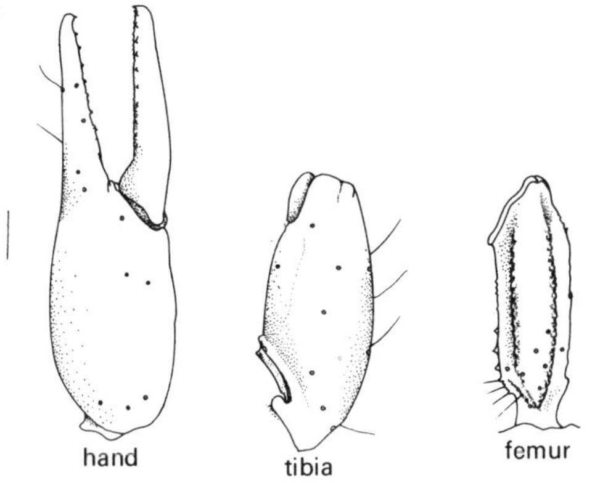

74

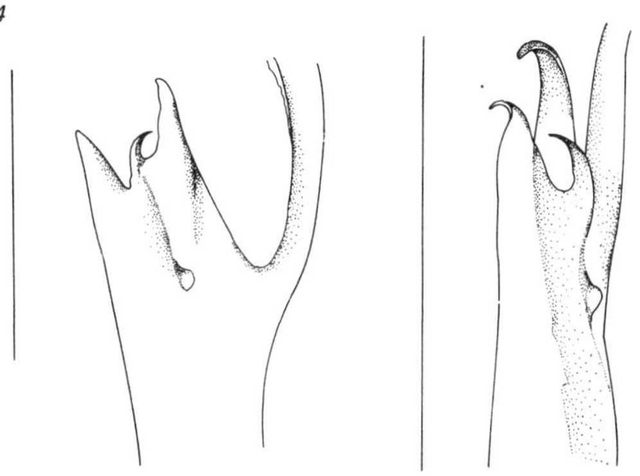

Figs. 73–74: *Buthacus leptochelys leptochelys* (Hemprich & Ehrenberg, 1829)
73. pedipalp, arrangement of trichobothria; 74. paraxial organ, form of lobes at base of flagellum; scale-lines 1 mm

Pectines: Long, extending beyond coxo-trochanteral articulation of leg IV, also in females; number of denticles in females from Israel 21–26 (usually 24–26), from Sinai 26–29; males from Israel with 29–35 (usually 30–32) denticles, from Sinai with 33–35 denticles.

Pedipalps: Femur relatively slender, smooth except on inner side; hand of male 1.4 times longer and wider than hand of female; hand of male distinctly wider than tibia, narrower than tibia in female; movable finger of female 1.5–2 times longer than hand, less than 1.5 times longer in males; fingers usually shorter than prosoma or almost of same length; outer accessory denticles near all series of denticles of movable finger, one or two denticles sometimes lacking.

Walking Legs: Margin of coxae smooth in females; outer tooth of basitarsal spur of legs III and IV with up to 12 bristles in specimens from Israel and with up to 20 bristles in specimens from Sinai; dorsal combs of basitarsus and tibia of leg III usually with more than 10 long bristles.

Measurements (mm): *Female*. Adult, Palmaẖim (No. Sc. 1534). Total length 60; prosoma 6, mesosoma 18, metasoma 36. Segments of metasoma: first L3.3, W3.5,

H3.0; second 4.6–3.3–2.9; third 4.8–3.2–2.9; fourth 4.9–2.7–2.5; fifth 6.0–2.7–2.5. Vesicule (including pedicel) L3.2, W2.2; pedicel W1.3; aculeus L3.7. Pedipalps: femur L4.3, W1.6; tibia L5.7, W2.2; hand L2.8, W1.9; movable finger L5.0. Number of denticles of pectine 24–25.

Male. Adult, Palmahim (No. Sc. 1353). Total length 61; prosoma 5.8, mesosoma 15, metasoma 40. Segments of metasoma: first L4.0, W3.7, H3.2; second 5.2–3.6–3.0; third 5.4–3.4–2.9; fourth 5.6–2.8–2.5; fifth 6.6–2.7–2.4. Vesicule (including pedicel) L3.4, W2.1; pedicel W1.3; aculeus L3.8. Pedipalps: femur L4.9, W1.7; tibia L5.9, W2.3; hand L4.3, W2.7; movable finger L4.8. Number of denticles of pectine 34–34.

Distribution: Africa: Lower Egypt, southern Libya, Chad, Niger, southern Algeria,

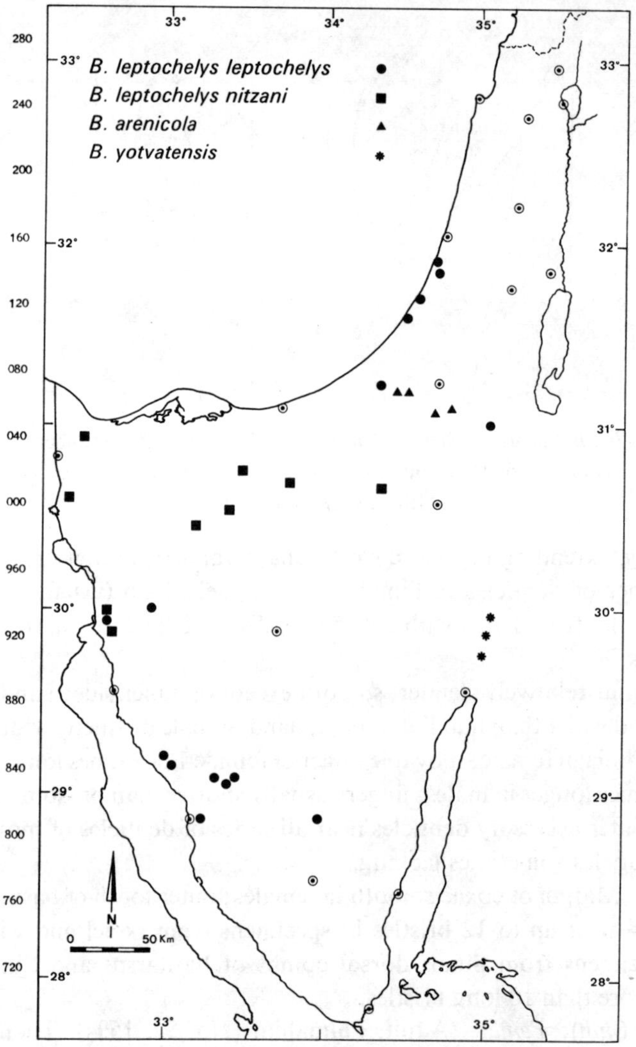

Map 6: Records of *Buthacus* in Israel and Sinai

southern Morocco. The definite position of specimens from Morocco is uncertain; they apparently belong to *B. l. leptochelys*. Asia: ?Iran. Birula (1905) described some specimens from Arabistan and identified them as *B. tadmorensis*. Whether they belong to *B. l. leptochelys*, like Simon's *tadmorensis* from Palmyra, is not known. The references of the following records are summarized in the Appendix on Distribution. Iraq: Tel Afar west of Mosul, Makhmoor. Syria: Palmyra. ?Jordan: Juvenile specimens from Wadi Deba' 100 km southeast of Amman.

Israel and Sinai (Map 6): Simon (1892) gives the following localities for *B. leptochelys*: Jericho, wadis on the west shore of the Dead Sea, Tiberias. However, *B. leptochelys* has not been found again in these localities. Many specimens were discovered in the sand dunes of the southern Coastal Plain of Israel, in the vicinity of Ashqelon. The dunes north of the Rubin River were searched several times, but *B. leptochelys* was not found there, whereas on the south bank of the river the species is quite common. The Rubin River is thus considered as the northern border of distribution of the genus *Buthacus* along the Mediterranean coast. Specimens were also found in inland sandy soils near Mamshit, 35 km southeast of Be'er Sheva'. There is also a juvenile specimen from Naẖal Ẕin, southern Negev, which may be *B. leptochelys*. Another population of *B. l. leptochelys* occurs in southern Sinai, along the western shores.

Ecological Notes: *Buthacus leptochelys leptochelys* is fairly common. It is found along the Mediterranean in brown-red sandy soils alternating with 'kurkar' and in the coastal sand dunes. It is usually buried in the sand or under large objects. It was found moving on steep slopes of drifting sand dunes and, occasionally, close to the sea front. It preys on small insects.

Buthacus leptochelys nitzani Levy, Amitai & Shulov, 1973

Figs. 75–78; Map 6

Zool. J. Linn. Soc. Lond., 52: 126. Type Locality: Ẕe'elim, northern Negev, Israel; type (female. No. Sc. 280) deposited in the Hebrew University, Jerusalem.

Coloration: Body light yellow, with orange on anterior part of prosoma dorsally and on anterior part of segments 1–4 of metasoma; whole fifth segment of metasoma reddish orange; pedipalps: femur, proximal part of tibia and proximal parts of walking legs reddish orange. *Size*: Adults less than 5 cm long.

Prosoma: Median eyes large, separated from each other by more than their diameter in females, by less than the diameter of one median eye in males; lateral eyes distinct, combined length of all three lateral eyes equalling diameter of median eye in females, less than this in males.

Mesosoma: Tergites smooth in females, slightly granulate in males, mainly laterally; crests of tergites indistinct.

Metasoma: Intermediary crests of second segment extending to half of segment in females, ending before middle of segment in males; intermediary crests of third segment with only 4–5 granules; latero-ventral crests of third segment with medium-

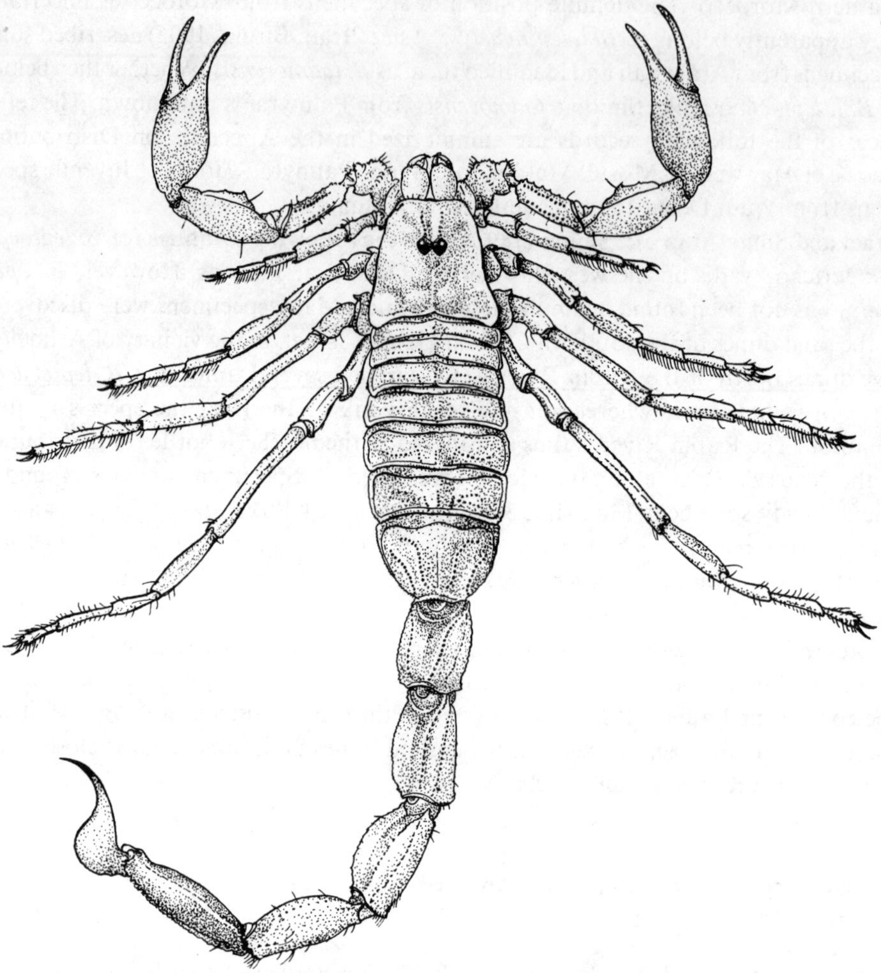

Fig. 75: *Buthacus leptochelys nitzani* Levy, Amitai & Shulov, 1973
Male from Revivim, Israel (Sc. 1991); total length 44 mm

sized teeth, distinct throughout; axial and ventral crests of fifth segment distinct, with pointed, spaced granules; latero-ventral crests of fifth segment with large, slightly crescent-shaped teeth and smaller teeth between them; posterior ventral margin of fifth segment with 7–9 relatively large teeth; segments 2–5 in females and 4–5 in males shagreened ventrally; vesicule granulate ventrally in females, smooth in males.

Pectines: Relatively short, not extending beyond coxo-trochanteral articulation of leg IV in females, but extending beyond this articulation in males; females with 18–22 (usually 19–21) denticles, males with 26–30 (usually 27–28) denticles.

Pedipalps: Femur relatively short, smooth, except for slight granulation on inner side in females, also with small granules dorsally in males; tibia smooth, without crests; hand of male 1.4 times longer and wider than hand of female; hand distinctly

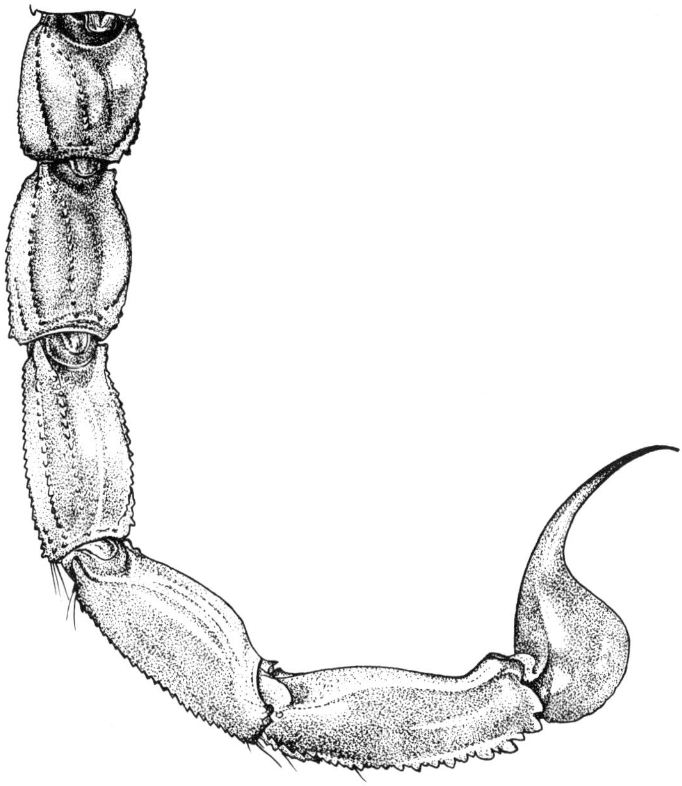

Fig. 76: *Buthacus leptochelys nitzani* Levy, Amitai & Shulov, 1973
Metasoma, length 30 mm

wider than tibia in male, narrower than tibia in female; fingers shorter than prosoma; movable finger with 8–9 series of denticles; outer accessory denticles present near all series of denticles, sometimes one or two denticles near anterior series absent.
Walking Legs: Margin of coxae smooth in females, with slightly granulate crests in males; outer tooth of basitarsal spur of legs III and IV with up to 12 bristles; dorsal comb of tibia of leg III with 8–10 bristles, comb of basitarsus with 12–16 bristles.
Measurements (mm): *Female.* Adult, Ẕe'elim (No. Sc. 280). Total length 47; prosoma 5.2, mesosoma 12, metasoma 30. Segments of metasoma: first L3.4, W3.2, H2.7; second 4.0–3.1–2.8; third 4.0–3.0–2.7; fourth 4.0–2.5–2.3; fifth 5.0–2.6–2.3. Vesicule (including pedicel) L2.8, W1.9; pedicel W1.2; aculeus (slightly damaged) L3.1. Pedipalps: femur L3.6, W1.5; tibia L4.7, W2.0; hand L2.7, W1.7; movable finger L4.1. Number of denticles of pectine 21–22.
Male. Adult, dunes north of Revivim (No. Sc. 1989). Total length 46; prosoma 4.6, mesosoma 12, metasoma 30. Segments of metasoma: first L3.1, W2.9, H2.4; second 3.9–2.8–2.4; third 4.1–2.7–2.3; fourth 4.2–2.1–2.0; fifth 5.0–2.2–2.0. Vesicule (including pedicel) L2.5, W1.7; pedicel W1.2; aculeus L3.0. Pedipalps: femur L3.8, W1.4; tibia L4.7, W2.0; hand L3.5, W2.3; movable finger L3.8. Number of denticles of pectine 29–30.

77

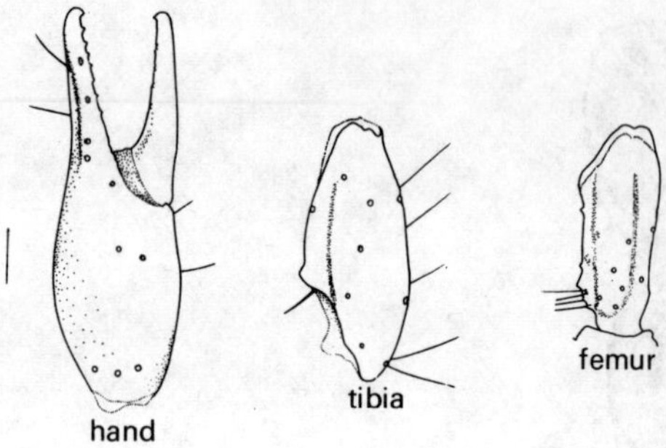

78

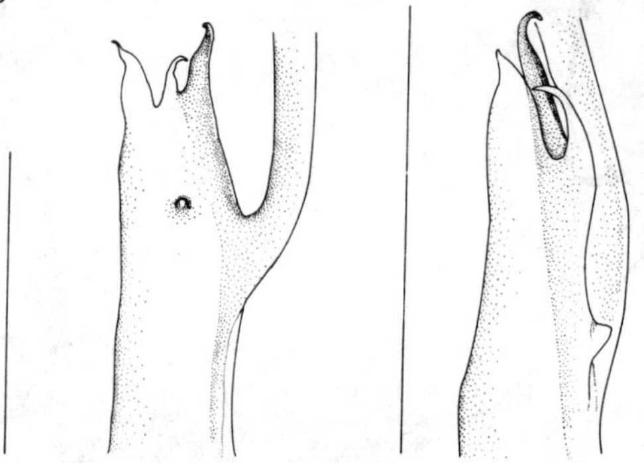

Figs. 77–78: *Buthacus leptochelys nitzani* Levy, Amitai & Shulov, 1973
77. pedipalp, arrangement of trichobothria; 78. paraxial organ, form of lobes at base of flagellum; scale-lines 1 mm

Distribution, Israel (Map 6; p. 82): *Buthacus leptochelys nitzani* was found only in the dunes of H̱aluẕa, southwest of Be'er Sheva' in the northern Negev.
Ecological Note: *Buthacus leptochelys nitzani* is rare. It is found on loess soil and on sand dunes in the desert.

Buthacus arenicola (Simon, 1885)
Figs. 79–81; Map 6

Buthus arenicola Simon, 1885, *Exploration scientifique de la Tunisie*, Paris: 50–52. Type Locality: Tunisia.
Buthus leptochelys (Hemprich & Ehrenberg, 1829). Pocock, 1895, *J. Linn. Soc.* (*Zool.*) *Lond.*, 25: 299–300 (in part).
Buthacus arenicola—. Vachon, 1949, *Archs Inst. Pasteur Algér.*, 27(1): 71.

Description based on specimens from northern Sinai.
Coloration: Uniformly yellow. *Size*: Adults about 6 cm long.
Prosoma: Median eyes large, separated from each other by more than their diameter;

lateral eyes small, combined length of all three lateral eyes only slightly exceeding diameter of one median eye.

Mesosoma: Crests of tergites only slightly indicated, from third or fourth segment onwards.

Metasoma: Intermediary crests of second segment not extending to half of segment, and with only 2–4 granules on third segment; latero-ventral crests of third segment almost smooth in anterior half of segment and with small, almost regular teeth posteriorly; ventral crests of fifth segment indistinct, but axial crests with a double row of distinct, small, spaced granules throughout; latero-ventral crests of fifth segment with irregular triangular teeth of varying size; posterior ventral margin of fifth segment with 9–12 small teeth which are smaller than the lateral anal lobes; anal lobes reduced, usually only two of three projecting; vesicule shagreened ventrally near pedicel and with small depressions; fourth and, mainly, fifth segments sometimes shagreened ventrally.

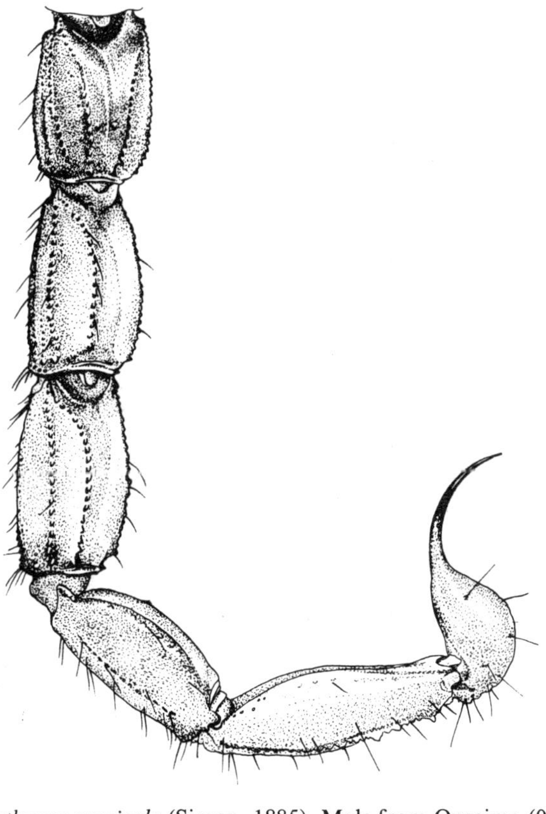

Fig. 79: *Buthacus arenicola* (Simon, 1885). Male from Quseima (004/083), Sinai (Sc. 2077); metasoma, length 34 mm

80

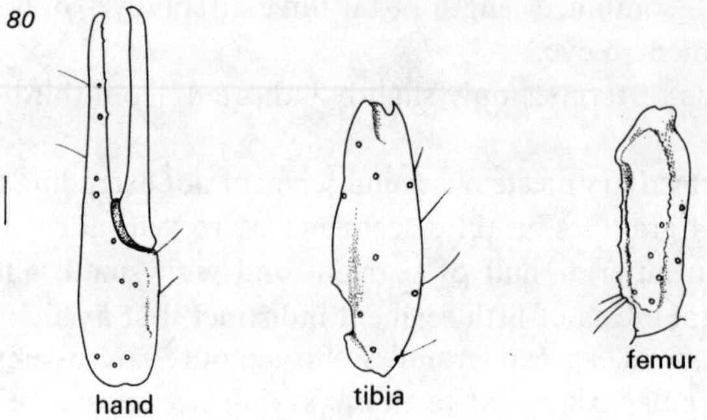

81

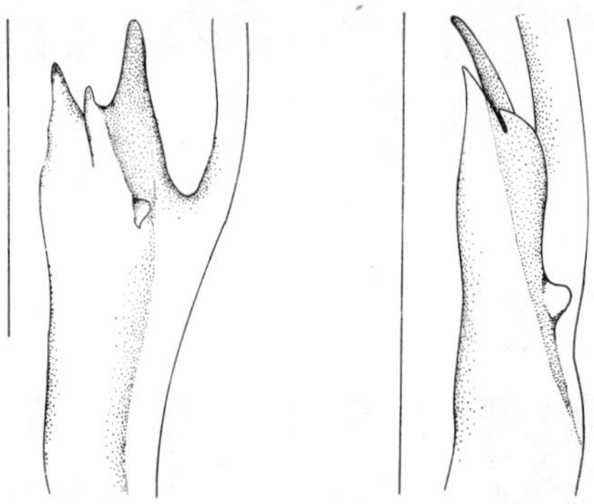

Figs. 80–81: *Buthacus arenicola* (Simon, 1885)
80. pedipalp, arrangement of trichobothria; 81. paraxial organ, form of lobes at base of flagellum; scale-lines 1 mm

Pectines: Long, extending beyond coxo-trochanteral articulation of leg IV, also in females; females with 26–29 denticles, males with 31–35 denticles.
Pedipalps: Femur relatively slender, smooth except on inner side; hand of male about as long and wide as hand of female; hand narrower than tibia in both sexes; movable finger more than twice as long as hand in both sexes; fingers about as long as prosoma; outer accessory denticles absent near most series of denticles, at most 1–3 denticles near basal series.
Walking Legs: Margin of coxae slightly granulate or with slightly indicated crests; outer tooth of basitarsal spur of legs III and IV with up to 24 bristles; dorsal combs of basitarsus and tibia of leg III usually with more than 10 long bristles.
Measurements (mm): *Female*. Adult, Bir Gifgafa, Sinai (No. Sc. 1251). Total length 62; prosoma 6, mesosoma 19, metasoma 37. Segments of metasoma: first L4.1, W3.5, H2.9; second 4.9–3.4–2.9; third 5.1–3.2–2.8; fourth 5.2–2.7–2.5; fifth 6.4–2.6–2.4. Vesicule (including pedicel) L3.1, W1.9; pedicel W1.3; aculeus L3.9. Pedipalps: femur L5.1, W1.7; tibia L6.5, W2.2; hand L2.8, W1.8; movable finger L6.1. Number of denticles of pectine 27–27.

Male. Adult, Quseima, Sinai (No. Sc. 2077). Total length 53; prosoma 5.2, mesosoma 14, metasoma 34. Segments of metasoma: first L3.7, W3.2, H2.5; second 4.5–3.1–2.6; third 4.5–2.9–2.4; fourth 5.0–2.3–2.2; fifth 5.5–2.2–2.0. Vesicule (including pedicel) L3.0, W1.6; pedicel W1.2; aculeus L3.5. Pedipalps: femur L4.6, W1.5; tibia L5.5, W1.9; hand L3.2, W1.8; movable finger L5.3. Number of denticles of pectine 31–31.

Distribution: Populations without a clear-cut range of distribution are found in southern Algeria, southern Tunisia, Central Libya and Egypt (in the British Museum there is a specimen from the west bank of the Suez Canal – *leg*. Anderson, 1894). Simon (1892) recorded *B. arenicola* from wadis west of the Dead Sea and from Palmyra in the Syrian Desert. However, no specimens from these localities are present in his collection.

Northern Sinai (Map 6, p. 82): *Buthacus arenicola* occurs only in northern Sinai from about Quseima in the east to Qantara in the west, and extends south to about opposite the city of Suez.

Ecological Note: *Buthacus arenicola* is known in our area only from a few specimens. It is found in sand dunes in the desert.

Systematic Remarks: Simon (1885) described *B. arenicola* from Tunisia (Tozzer, Gabès) and added that this species was also found in Algeria (Bou-Saada, Biskra, Debila) and in Lower Egypt (Ramleh, Port Said; *leg*. A. Letourneux). However, later, Pocock (1895), Kraepelin (1899) and also Simon (1910) considered *B. arenicola* to be a synonym of *B. leptochelys*. Birula (1908) regarded only Simon's Egyptian specimens as synonymous with *B. leptochelys*. Moreover, Birula (1911), in describing *Buthacus spatzi* from Algeria, knew of Simon's (1910) statement; however, he made a precise distinction between *B. spatzi* and Simon's (1885) *B. arenicola*. Birula (1914) placed specimens from Algeria in a different subspecies, *B. leptochelys arenicola*. Pallary (1938) reinstated *B. arenicola* but without sufficient diagnostic basis. Vachon (1949), in view of the absence of a complement of outer accessory denticles on the fingers of the pedipalps, distinguished between *B. arenicola* and *B. leptochelys*. He considered *B. spatzi* a subspecies of *B. arenicola* because of certain differences in the number of outer denticles, a character which apparently varies so markedly that it is probably of more importance for the distinction of groups of species, than at the species level. *Buthacus arenicola* and *B. spatzi* can usually be distinguished by the form of the body and of the hand. Both forms occur in southern Tunisia and may thus possibly be different species. The population of *B. spatzi* in Tunisia differs from that in Algeria, each perhaps representing different subspecies.

Buthacus arenicola and *B. leptochelys* occur in the same area on the east bank of the Suez Canal, opposite the city of Suez, but no intermediate population has been found. A similar situation probably exists in North Africa. Populations of *B. arenicola* and *B. leptochelys* are close together in southern Algeria (Tassili n'Ajjer). *Buthacus arenicola* from Sinai differs slightly from the North African specimens, but there are probably different subspecies of *B. arenicola*. The occurrence of *B. arenicola* in the region of Sinai and Egypt is a new record. Hitherto, Central Libya was considered as the easternmost border of this species.

Buthacus yotvatensis Levy, Amitai & Shulov, 1973

Figs. 82–85; Map 6

Zool. J. Linn. Soc. Lond., 52: 130. Type Locality: Yotvata, Israel; type deposited in Tel Aviv University.

Coloration: Yellowish olive to light yellow. *Size*: Adults 6–9 cm long.

Prosoma: With dense, small granules, smooth only between and around median eyes; crests indistinct; median eyes situated slightly anterior to middle, separated from each other by more than their diameter; lateral eyes distinct, combined length of all three lateral eyes less than the diameter of one median eye.

Mesosoma: Tergites with dense, small granules, mainly laterally and on posterior parts; crests distinct from second or third segment onwards; all sternites smooth and shining.

Metasoma: Slender, first segment widest, segments gradually narrowing posteriorly; all segments longer than wide or high; dense rows of long bristles along dorsal crests, only a few bristles between crests; rows of bristles along latero-dorsal crests only on fifth segment; first segment with 10 complete crests; intermediary crests of second segment not extending to half of segment in males, ending before middle of segment in females; intermediary crests of third segment with 3–4 granules only in posterior part of segment; fourth segment with at most one granule in posterior part; latero-ventral crests of segment 1 indistinct, smooth, with only a few fused granules in posterior part; crests of second segment slightly indicated, smooth anteriorly with fused granules posteriorly; crests more or less distinct on segments 3–4, with regular fused granules; latero-ventral crests of fifth segment with irregular

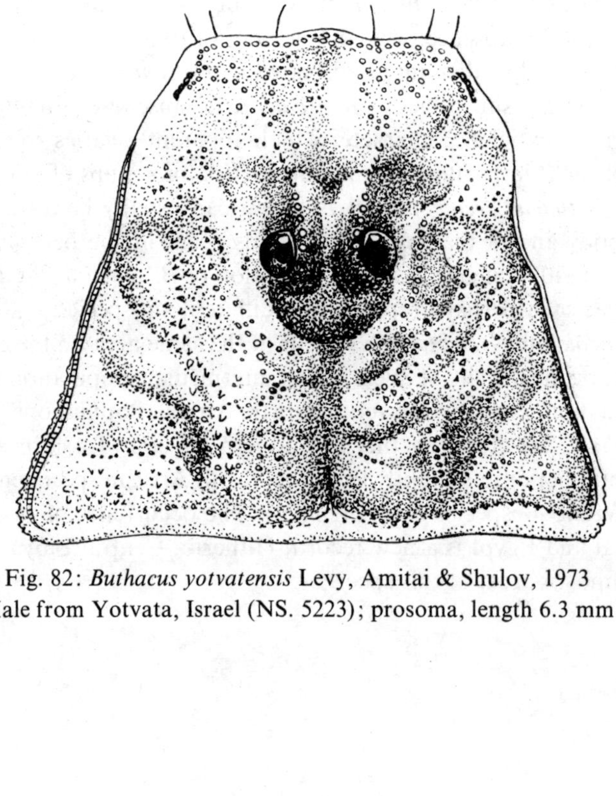

Fig. 82: *Buthacus yotvatensis* Levy, Amitai & Shulov, 1973
Male from Yotvata, Israel (NS. 5223); prosoma, length 6.3 mm

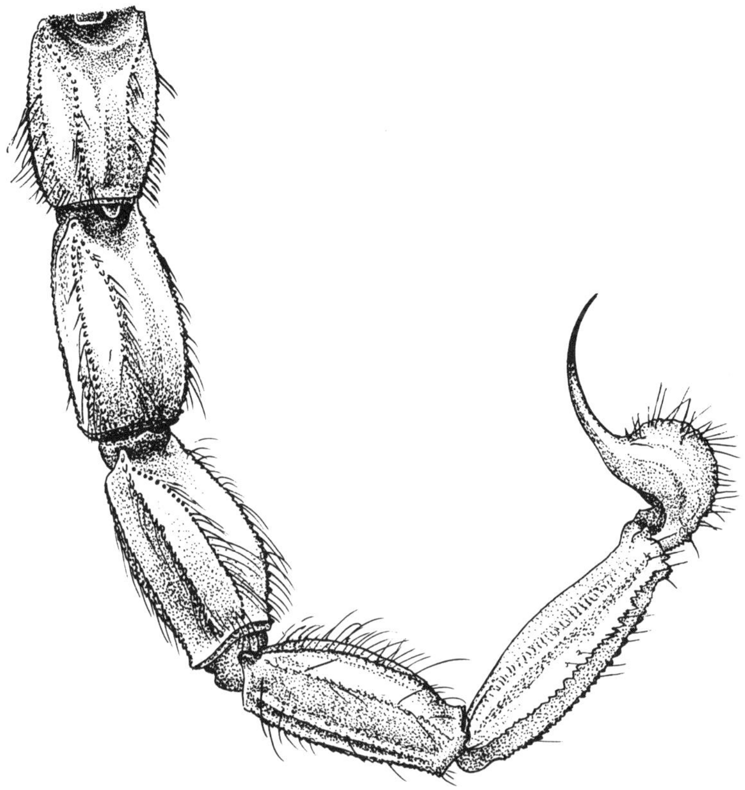

Fig. 83: *Buthacus yotvatensis* Levy, Amitai & Shulov, 1973. Metasoma, length 42 mm

teeth which are smaller anteriorly, large and small teeth irregularly alternating posteriorly; latero-ventral and ventral crests of all segments not accompanied by rows of bristles; ventral crests of fifth segment with a few spaced granules, axial crest distinct, slightly raised, with regular granules; posterior ventral margin of segment 5 with about 10 almost fused teeth; fifth segment with two lateral anal lobes; vesicule slender, narrower than fifth segment, smooth dorsally, granulate ventrally, mainly near pedicel; aculeus thin, very long, longer than vesicule including pedicel; fifth segment with a latero-basal row of 7–9 bristles; anal margin of fifth segment with five bristles; stinger with many bristles.

Pectines: Extending distinctly beyond coxo-trochanteral articulation in females, almost to trochanter of leg IV in males; outer side with hairs, inner fulcra without hairs; females with 25–28 denticles, males with 33–34 denticles (males from Syria with 30–31 denticles).

Pedipalps: Femur slender, about three times longer than wide, slightly shagreened dorsally and with numerous outer accessory bristles; tibia smooth on all sides, slender, about three times as long as wide, without outer accessory bristles; hand smooth, without crests, slightly narrower than tibia; fingers without recess at base,

84

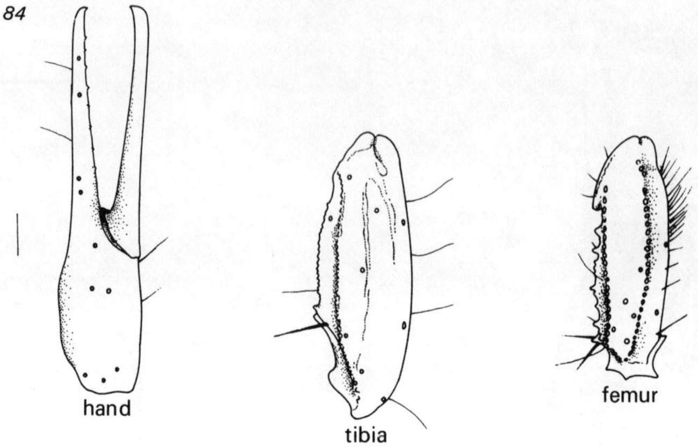

85

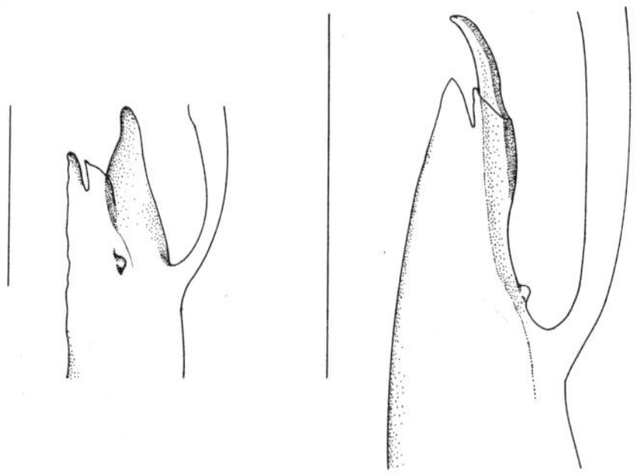

Figs. 84–85: *Buthacus yotvatensis* Levy, Amitai & Shulov, 1973
84. pedipalp, arrangement of trichobothria; 85. paraxial organ, form of lobes at base of flagellum; scale-lines 1 mm

about as long as prosoma; fingers about twice as long as hand; movable finger with 10 series of denticles, outer accessory denticles present near all series; four denticles under apical tooth of movable finger.

Walking Legs: Outer tooth of basitarsal spur simple, with numerous bristles on leg III; dorsal comb of tibia of leg III with 11–15 long bristles, comb of basitarsus with 15–25 long bristles; coxae of all legs shagreened and with a granulate crest anteriorly; sole of tarsi with long, thin bristles not arranged in rows.

Measurements (mm): *Female.* Adult, dunes of Yotvata (No. Sc. 2333). Total length 76; prosoma 8.0, mesosoma 16, metasoma 52. Segments of metasoma: first L6.5, W4.8, H4.2; second 7.0–4.5–4.3; third 7.0–4.3–4.1; fourth 7.2–3.8–3.6; fifth 8.5–3.8–3.3. Vesicule (including pedicel) L4.2, W3.1; pedicel W1.8; aculeus L5.2. Pedipalps: femur L6.1, W2.3; tibia L7.5, W2.6; hand L3.8, W2.3; movable finger L7.7. Number of denticles of pectine 26–26.

Male. Adult, dunes of Yotvata (No. NS. 5223, Tel Aviv University). Total length 64; prosoma 6.3, mesosoma 16, metasoma 42. Segments of metasoma: first L5.0, W4.0,

H3.4; second 5.5–3.8–3.5; third 5.8–3.6–3.4; fourth 6.0–3.2–2.9; fifth 7.1–3.0–2.5. Vesicule (including pedicel) L3.6, W2.2; pedicel W1.5; aculeus L3.9. Pedipalps: femur L5.6, W1.8; tibia L6.8, W2.2; hand L3.3, W2.1; movable finger L6.2. Number of denticles of pectine 33–34.
Distribution: Syria: Abu Hareira, probably near the Euphrates. ?Iraq: Definite systematic position of a species from Hinaidi uncertain. ?Iran (Personal communication of Dr Farzanpay).
Israel (Map 6, p. 82): *Buthacus yotvatensis* is found only in the sand dunes along the 'Arava Valley, southern Israel.
Ecological Note: Populations of *B. yotvatensis* are found in small restricted areas in inland sand dunes in the desert.

Genus ORTHOCHIRUS Karsch, 1891

Berl. Ent. Z., 36(2) : 306

Orthodactylus Karsch, 1881, *Berl. Ent. Z.*, 25:90 (non Hitchcock 1858); preocc.
Butheolus Simon, 1882. Simon, 1889, *Verh. Zool.-Bot. Ges. Wien*, 39 : 386.
Orthochirus Karsch, 1891, *Berl. Ent. Z.*, 36(2) : 306; name to replace *Orthodactylus*.
Orthochirus—. Simon, 1910, *Bull. Soc. Ent. Égypte*: 77–78.

Type Species: *Androctonus scrobiculosus* Grube, 1873 (as *Orthodactylus olivaceus* Karsch, 1881).

Diagnosis: Prosoma without crests but with depressions behind median eyes: posterior segments of metasoma with small depressions.

Prosoma: Granulate or smooth; area between median eyes and posterior margin of prosoma with a deep concavity indented by grooves and depressions; median eyes separated from each other by more than their diameter.
Mesosoma: Tergites smooth or granulate, with or without crests.
Metasoma: Short and thick, wider posteriorly; segments concave dorsally; fifth segment without distinct lateral anal lobes; vesicule small and slender.
Pectines: Anterior margin of sternal plate deeply incised at middle; inner fulcra without hairs, at most with a small sclerotized point.
Pedipalps: Crests on tibia more or less distinct; hand without crests; fingers with or without outer accessory denticles near series of denticles; three or four denticles under apical tooth of movable finger.
Walking Legs: Outer tooth of basitarsal spur simple, with only a few hairs; basitarsus of three anterior legs always with a dorsal comb of bristles; sole of tarsi with short bristles or hairs.

Review of Genus: The species of *Orthochirus* are small, usually less than 5 cm long, many only about 3 cm long. The genus has a wide distribution from southern

Morocco to Egypt, Sudan and Eritrea and from the Mediterranean to India, Iran and east of the Caspian Sea.

Karsch (1886) stated that *Butheolus aristidis* Simon (1882) from Nubia in Sudan is closely related to *Orthodactylus,* but apparently belongs to another genus. Simon, Kraepelin, Birula, Pocock and others synonymized *Orthodactylus* with *Butheolus* (1882). However, Simon (1910) accepted Karsch's opinion and the name *Orthochirus.* He also stated that all species of *Butheolus* should be placed in the genus *Orthochirus,* except the type species *B. thalassinus* from Aden.

Many species and local forms of *Orthochirus* have been described. However, Birula stated that there is probably only one species, *O. scrobiculosus,* with numerous local forms. A revision of the genus is certainly necessary. Only *O. conchini* and *O. glabrifrons* have distinct characters; *O. scrobiculosus* and *O. bicolor* have many local forms with a great variation of characters. The above two species can usually be distinguished by the form of the fifth segment of the metasoma, but there may be intermediate forms.

Orthochirus scrobiculosus scrobiculosus (Grube, 1873)	Central Asia; northeast Iran
O. s. melanurus (Kessler, 1876) [= ? *fuscipes* (Pocock, 1900)]	Transcaspia
O. s. concolor Birula, 1899	Turkestan, Buchara
O. s. persa Birula, 1900b	Iran
O. s. mesopotamicus Birula, 1918	Iraq
O. s. negebensis (Shulov & Amitai, 1960)	Israel, Jordan, Sinai
Orthochirus conchini Simon (1889)	Transcaspia
Orthochirus bicolor bicolor (Pocock, 1897)	Afghanistan, Pakistan and northwest India
O. b. pallidus (Pocock, 1897	Afghanistan, Pakistan and northwest India
O. b. flavescens (Pocock, 1897)	Afghanistan, Pakistan and northwest India
O. b. insularis (Pocock, 1899a)	Socotra
?*Orthochirus luteipes* Roewer, 1943	India
Orthochirus glabrifrons (Kraepelin, 1903)	Muscat
Orthochirus aristidis Simon (1882)	Upper Egypt, Sudan, ? Somalia
Orthochirus innesi Simon, 1910 (= *seurati* Pallary, 1929)	Lower Egypt to North Africa

Orthochirus scrobiculosus (Grube, 1873)

Androctonus scrobiculosus Grube, 1873, *Jber. Schles. Ges. Vaterl. Kult.*: 56–57. Type Locality: Lenkora, Transcaucasia.

Androctonus melanurus Kessler, 1876, *Trudy Russk. Ent. Obshch.,* 8 : 16, pl. 1, figs. 1–3. Type Locality: Ust-urt, Kizyl-kum, Transcaspia.

Buthus schneideri L. Koch, 1878, *Naturw. Ges. Isis,* Dresden: 35–71. Type Locality: Krasnovodsk, east of Caspian Sea; deposited in the British Museum; examined.
Orthodactylus olivaceus Karsch, 1881, *Berl. Ent. Z.*, 25 : 89–91. Type Locality: Sicily.
Orthodactylus schneideri—. Karsch, 1886, *Berl. Ent. Z.*, 30 : 75.
Butheolus schneideri—. Simon, 1889, *Verh. Zool.-Bot. Ges. Wien,* 39 : 386.
Butheolus melanurus—. Pocock, 1890, *Proc. Zool. Soc. Lond.*, p. 121.
Orthochirus melanurus—. Pocock, 1895, *J. Linn. Soc. (Zool.) Lond.*, 25 : 295.
Butheolus scrobiculosus—. Birula, 1909, *Zool. Anz.*, 34 : 356–359.
Orthochirus scrobiculosus—. Birula, 1917, *Ann. Caucasian Mus.* (A;5), *Isr. Progr. Sci. Transl.*, Jerusalem, 1964 : 131.

Prosoma: As for the genus.
Mesosoma: Tergites usually densely granulate, rarely smooth laterally; seventh sternite with four crests which usually consist of several rows of granules.
Metasoma: Segments usually distinctly wider than long, sometimes fifth segment of varying length/width ratio; fifth segment without lateral projecting processes latero-ventrally on posterior part; depressions on posterior segments always distinct and not covered by adjacent granules.
Pedipalps: Femur without medio-basal trichobothrium dorsally (d_2 of Vachon, 1948) sometimes present but markedly reduced.
Systematic Remarks: *Orthochirus scrobiculosus* has many local forms with a great variation of characters. The distribution of *O. scrobiculosus* extends from Transcaspia throughout Iran and Iraq to Jordan, southern Israel and Sinai. The question as to whether it extends into Africa raises the problem of the systematic position of the African *O. aristidis–innesi* group. It is not certain whether these are different species or, as Birula (1927) and Whittick (1947) have suggested, subspecies of *O. scrobiculosus*. Together with specimens of the ordinary *O. scrobiculosus* from Iran and Iraq, other specimens were found which closely resemble *O. aristidis* from the Sudan. The subspecies in southern Israel and Sinai, apparently at the peripheral range of *O. scrobiculosus,* shows less resemblance to *O. aristidis*.
Examination of material from Lower Egypt (Gebel Mokattam, Cairo, Helwan, Siwa Oasis), Libya and Algeria proves that *O. innesi* closely resembles the form in Sinai and southern Israel. The only apparent difference between the Asian and African populations is the width of the posterior segments of the metasoma. In *O. scrobiculosus* (also in the specimens from Israel) the posterior segment of the metasoma is usually wider than long, while in *O. innesi* and *O. aristidis* it is distinctly longer than wide. Apparently the metasoma of *O. innesi* is longer and more slender than in *O. scrobiculosus*. This slight difference thus supports Birula's view. *Orthochirus s. negebensis* from Sinai, southern Israel and Jordan, which certainly belongs to *O. scrobiculosus,* is apparently a valid subspecies.
Karsch (1881) described *O. olivaceus* from Sicily, but this record is doubtful. Karsch (1886) recorded the species from Krasnovodsk, east of the Caspian Sea, and from Jericho. Karsch's *O. olivaceus* has long since been synonymized with *O. scrobiculosus*, and Birula's use of the name *olivaceus* (1917) for the subspecies in our area seems unjustified.

Orthochirus scrobiculosus negebensis (Shulov & Amitai, 1960)
Figs. 86–90; Map 7

Orthodactylus olivaceus Karsch, 1881. Karsch, 1886, *Berl. Ent. Z.*, 30(1) : 75.
Butheolus aristidis Simon, 1882. Simon, 1892, *Revue Biol. Nord Fr.* (*Lille*), 5 : 84.
Butheolus melanurus (Kessler, 1876). Kraepelin, 1899, *Das Tierreich,* 8. Lief., Berlin : 35.
Butheolus aristidis—. Birula, 1908, *Sber. Akad. Wiss. Wien,* 117(2;1) : 145–147.
Orthochirus innesi Simon, 1910, *Bull. Soc. Ent. Égypte* : 79 (in part). Type Locality: Gebel Mokattam, near Cairo, Egypt; type deposited in the Muséum National, Paris; examined.
Orthochirus scrobiculosus olivaceus (Karsch, 1881). Birula, 1917, *Ann. Caucasian Mus.* (A;5), *Isr. Progr. Sci. Transl.*, Jerusalem, 1964 : 141.
Orthochirus innesi negebensis Shulov & Amitai, 1960, *Archs Inst. Pasteur Algér.*, 38(1):117–119. Type Locality: Wadi Nafha, Central Negev, Israel; type (female, No. Sc. 86) deposited in the Hebrew University, Jerusalem.

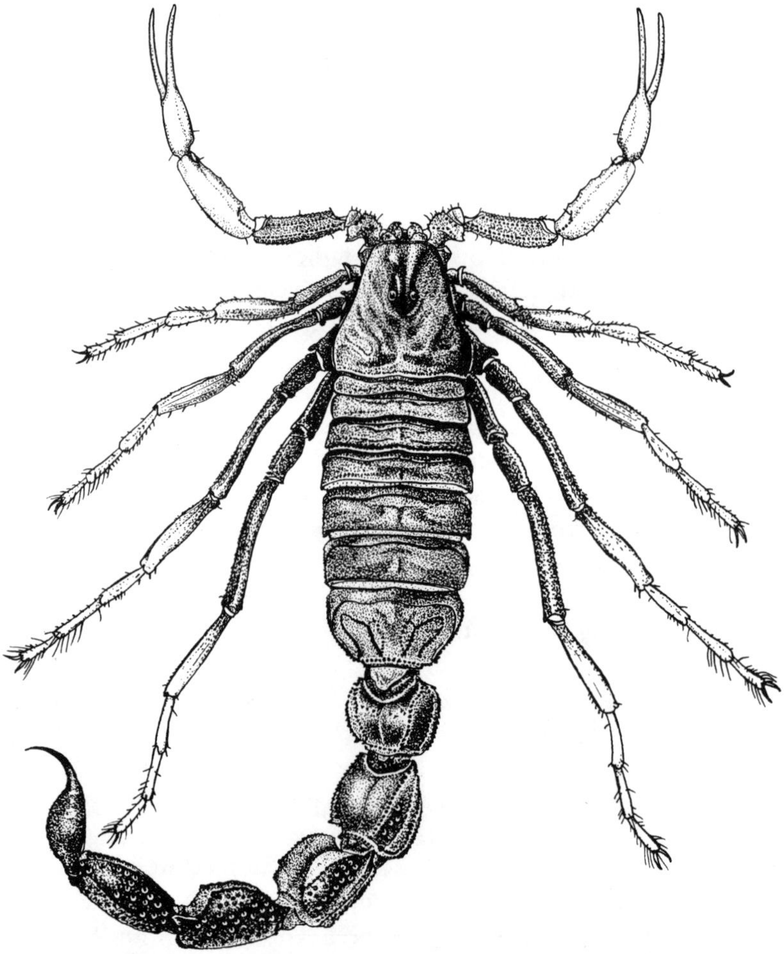

Fig. 86: *Orthochirus scrobiculosus negebensis* (Shulov & Amitai, 1960)
Male from 'En et Turaba (189/113), Israel (Sc. 642); total length 29 mm

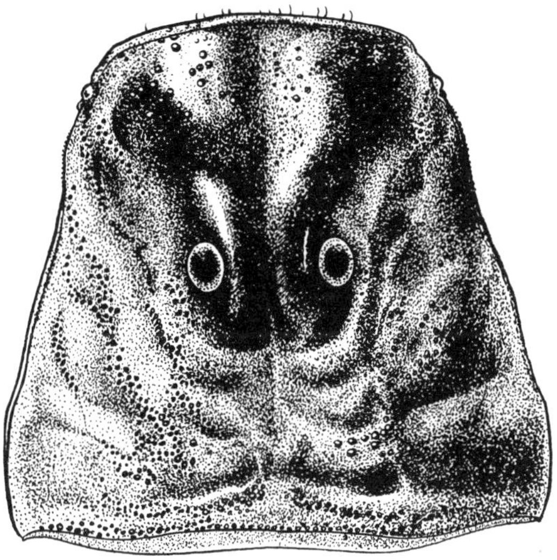

Fig. 87: *Orthochirus scrobiculosus negebensis* (Shulov & Amitai, 1960)
Prosoma, length 3.1 mm

Coloration: Black to blackish olive dorsally, brown to light brown ventrally, stinger reddish; pedipalps and legs dark on proximal segments (femur black, tibia blackish proximally and yellowish distally) and yellow on distal segments; pectines yellow.
Size: Length 2.5–4.0 cm.
Prosoma: Convex anteriorly; densely granulate, except space between median eyes and sometimes two smooth, shining spots anteriorly; depression behind median eyes densely granulate, except bottom of narrow transverse groove along posterior margin of prosoma; median eyes situated slightly anterior to middle.
Mesosoma: Tergites with dense, small granules, granulation densest in middle of tergites and crests usually indistinguishable; sternites 3–6, smooth in the middle, slightly shagreened laterally and near anterior margin.
Metasoma: Thick, widest on fourth and fifth segments, both of which are more or less of the same width; all segments wider than long, but fifth segment about as wide as long in males; segments 1–4 granulate dorsally, but granulation decreasing posteriorly; fifth segment slightly shagreened at bottom of posterior, dorsal, concave part and with a few granules anteriorly, lateral to concavity; axles of segments 1–4 densely shagreened dorsally, axle of fifth segment smooth; segments 1–2, and in males also segment 3, without small depressions dorsally, posterior segments with only a few shallow small depressions dorsally; granules of dorsal crests of segments 1–4 small and distinct; latero-dorsal crests of segments 1–2 in the form of raised lines with several rows of granules; segments 3–4 without latero-dorsal crests, but fifth segment with crests of granules extending to end of segment, or granules ending in middle of segment and crests continuing with a row of small depressions; third segment slightly granulate laterally and posteriorly and with a few shallow depressions; segments 4–5 with regularly distributed deep depressions laterally, space be-

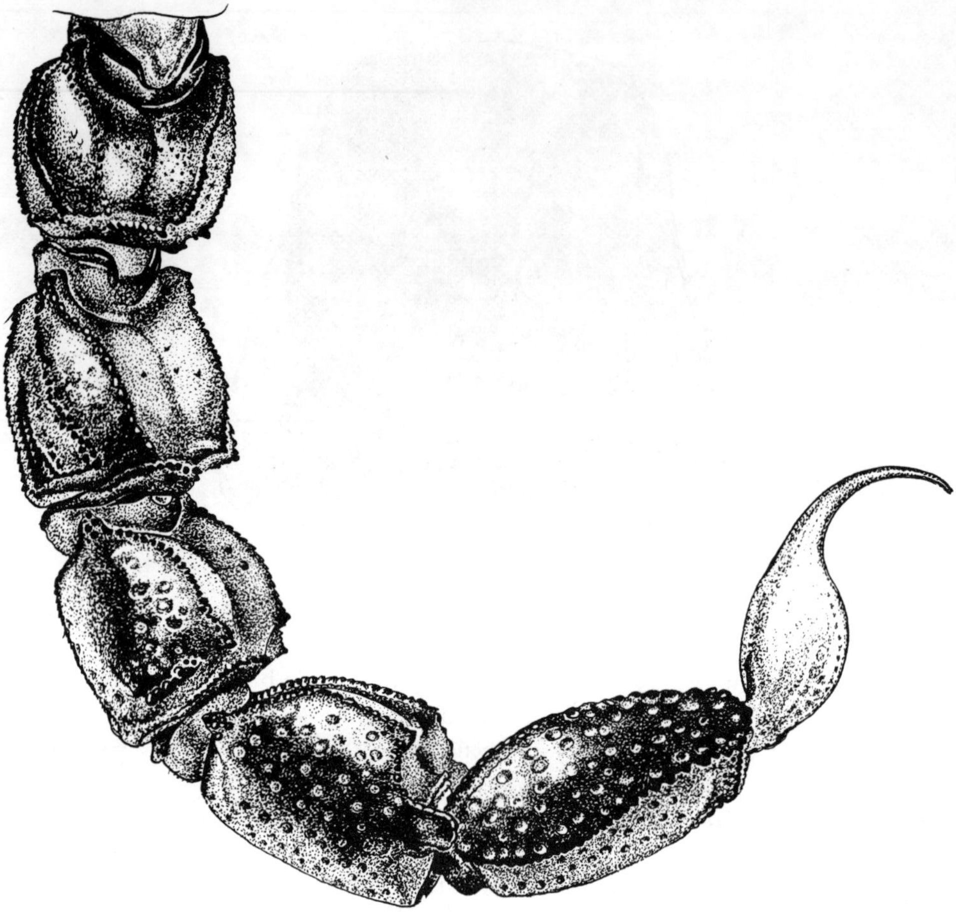

Fig. 88: *Orthochirus scrobiculosus negebensis* (Shulov & Amitai, 1960)
Metasoma, length 18 mm

tween depressions larger than their diameter, margin of depressions sometimes with small granules, or space between depressions smooth; segments 1–3 densely granulate ventrally with granulate ventral crests but without depressions; fourth segment with small depressions ventrally, margin of some of them with a few small granules; fifth segment with depressions ventrally, only on anterior two thirds of the segment, some of them surrounded by a few small granules, posterior third of segment with dense, distinct granulation, granulated area sometimes small; axial crest of fifth segment absent and latero-ventral crests distinct only in posterior third of segment; fifth segment distinctly more than twice as wide as vesicule; vesicule smooth dorsally, with small depressions ventrally and laterally.
Pectines: Not extending to coxo-trochanteral articulation of leg IV in females, extending slightly beyond articulation in males; outer side with short hairs; females with 15–19 (usually 16–18) denticles, males with 18–22 (usually 19–21) denticles.

89

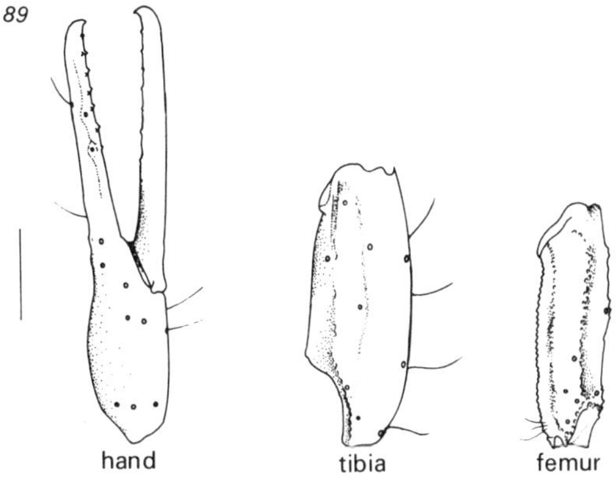

90

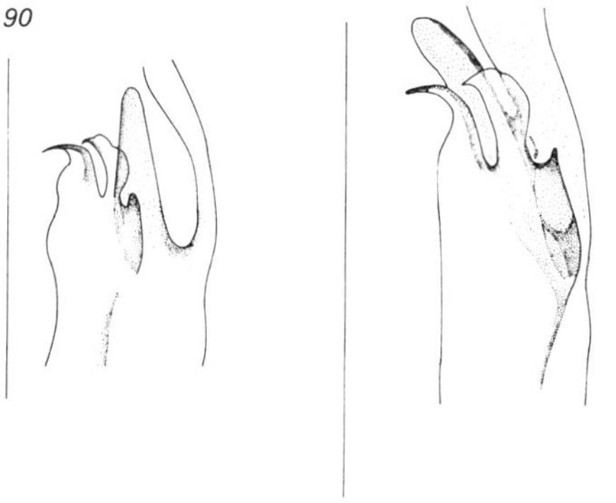

Figs. 89–90: *Orthochirus scrobiculosus negebensis* (Shulov & Amitai, 1960)
89. pedipalp, arrangement of trichobothria; 90. paraxial organ, form of lobes at base of flagellum; scale-lines 1 mm

Pedipalps: Femur with distinct crests; shagreened dorsally or with fine granulation, about three times longer than wide, slightly longer in males; medio-basal trichobothrium dorsally (d_2 of Vachon, 1948) usually absent, sometimes present but markedly reduced; femur with only a few short outer accessory bristles; tibia slender, smooth with smooth, distinct or only slightly indicated crests; pedicular tubercles not projecting; tibia about three times longer than wide, slightly shorter in females; 'inner length' of tibia distinctly exceeding its width; tibia without outer accessory bristles; hand smooth, slender, 1.5–1.7 times longer than wide, narrower than tibia; fingers slender, about twice as long as hand; movable finger with outer accessory denticles and with 8–9 series of denticles, sometimes with only one straight row at base of finger.
Walking Legs: Outer tooth of basitarsal spur simple, with 1–2 short hairs on leg IV; dorsal comb of basitarsus of leg III with 5–7 long bristles; sole of tarsi with short bristles in two rows.
Measurements (mm): *Female*. Adult, 'Arad (No. Sc. 641). Total length 36; prosoma 3.8, mesosoma 10.5, metasoma 21.7. Segments of metasoma: first L2.1, W3.4, H2.6;

second 2.6–3.4–2.6; third 2.9–3.6–2.9; fourth 3.3–3.8–3.0; fifth 3.7–3.8–2.8. Stinger (pedicel + vesicule + aculeus) L4.6; pedicel W1.1; vesicule W1.6. Pedipalps: femur L3.0, W1.0; tibia L3.6, W1.3; hand L1.8, W1.1; movable finger L3.4. Number of denticles of pectine 18–18.

Male. Adult, Jericho (No. Sc. 869). Total length 33; prosoma 3.5, mesosoma 9.0, metasoma 20.5. Segments of metasoma: first L1.9, W3.0, H2.2; second 2.4–3.1–2.3; third 2.7–3.3–2.5; fourth 3.1–3.4–2.6; fifth 3.5–3.4–2.4. Stinger (pedicel + vesicule + aculeus) L4.4; pedicel W1.0; vesicule W1.5. Pedipalps: femur L3.1, W0.8; tibia L3.6, W1.1; hand L1.8, W1.0; movable finger L3.6. Number of denticles of pectine 20–20.

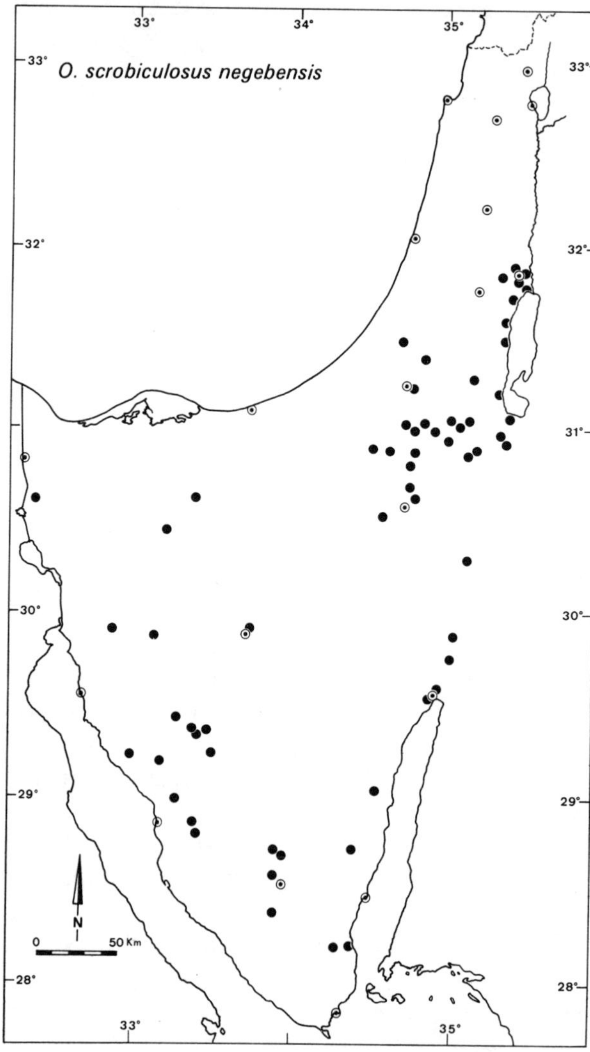

Map 7: Records of *Orthochirus* in Israel and Sinai

Distribution: Jordan: Qasr Amra (new record; specimen in the British Museum), location near Amman (new record; specimen at The Hebrew University, Jerusalem). Israel and Sinai (Map 7): References of previous records from Israel are summarized in the Appendix on Distribution; no specimens of *Orthochirus* have formerly been recorded from Sinai. *Orthochirus scrobiculosus* occurs throughout Sinai and southern Israel, extending north along the Judean Desert to Jericho. It is absent in the coastal zone, as well as in northern Sinai.

Ecological Notes: *Orthochirus scrobiculosus* is fairly common. It is found on loess soil and in the stony desert and is absent on terra rossa and brown rendzina. It lives under small stones. The metasoma is held curled, pressed to the back with the stinger completely hidden. It moves slowly, does not sting readily and can be kept in large numbers in containers without cannibalism. Parturition in May–September, mainly in June; number of young 5–12. It preys on small insects. It usually stings from the side; the sting is painful but produces no aftereffects.

Family SCORPIONIDAE Pocock, 1893

Ann. Mag. Nat. Hist. Lond., (6) 12 : 306

Type Genus: *Scorpio* Linnaeus, 1758.
Diagnosis: Sternum pentagonal; legs with only one outer basitarsal spur; aculeus without subaculear tubercle.

Werner (1934) recognized six subfamilies in the Scorpionidae. Only the Scorpioninae are represented in our region. Vachon (1973) lists 19 genera in the Scorpionidae; only one genus occurs in Israel.

Subfamily SCORPIONINAE Pocock, 1893

Ann. Mag. Nat. Hist. Lond., (6) 12 : 306

Diagnosis: Metasoma with a pair of ventral crests on segments 1–4; tarsi of legs with rounded latero-apical lobes; hand of pedipalp usually rounded dorsally.

Werner (1934) recorded four genera in the Scorpioninae: *Heterometrus* (Southeast Asia), *Pandinus* (mainly Equatorial Africa), *Opisthophthalmus* (South Africa and Ethiopian Region) and *Scorpio* (North Africa, Middle East to Iran and Arabia).

Genus SCORPIO Linnaeus, 1758

Systema Naturae, 10th ed. : 624

Type Species: *Scorpio maurus* Linnaeus, 1758; subsequent designation by Karsch, 1879, *Mitt. Munch. Ent. Ver.*, 3 : 16.

Diagnosis: Tibia of pedipalps with only three trichobothria ventrally; latero-apical lobes of tarsi of legs with more than two spines; anterior side of coxa of leg II smooth.

Prosoma: Anterior margin slightly incised in the middle; crests absent; narrow median groove passing through anterior part of prosoma to beyond median eyes; deep transverse groove passing along posterior margin, in the middle joining a short, deep groove which extends towards the median eyes; posterior part of prosoma with a triangular area formed by two dark lines extending towards median eyes from each end of transverse groove; two deep oblique folds extending to sides of prosoma from each end of transverse groove; three lateral eyes distinct, anterior eyes larger and closer to each other than to smaller posterior eye; sternum incised in middle of posterior margin.
Mesosoma: Tergites smooth, shagreened or granulate; all tergites except seventh without crests; genital operculum divided medially into two plates in males, only indented medially in females; seventh sternite with four crests.

Metasoma: Relatively short, narrower distally than at base; crests more or less distinct on all segments; vesicule granulate ventrally; aculeus short.
Pectines: Sternal plate of varying form; pectines short, outer side with hairs, inner fulcra with one fine hair.
Chelicerae: Immovable finger with three teeth on inner side, without teeth ventrally; movable finger with three or four teeth dorsally, without teeth ventrally.
Pedipalps: Femur thick, granulate dorsally; tibia thick, without pedicular tubercles; hand very broad, inner margin rounded, granulate dorsally, at least partially tuberculate or with a reticulate pattern of low ridges; fingers thick.
Walking Legs: Sole of tarsi with short spines in two rows extending to narrow latero-apical lobes situated lateral to claws; tarsi with a small dorsal finger-like process apically between claws.

Review of Genus: Linnaeus (1758) included five species in *Scorpio*: *maurus, afer, americus, europaeus* and *australis*. All species except *maurus* were later placed in other genera.
Hemprich & Ehrenberg (1829) established the subgenus *Heterometrus* of the genus *Buthus* for forms now considered to be subspecies of *Scorpio maurus*, and also for a different species from India. They were followed by Simon (1872), Pocock (1900a) and Pallary (1928, 1938), who placed these forms in *Heterometrus*. The genus *Scorpio* was reinstated by Karsch (1879), and Kraepelin (1899) later established the genus *Heterometrus* with the type species *H. spinifer* Hemprich & Ehrenberg from India. This is now generally accepted. The main difference between the two genera consists in the presence or absence of an area of granules and bristles on the anterior side of the coxa of leg II. This granulate area, sometimes named 'stridulation organ', is absent in *Scorpio maurus*.
Kraepelin (1899) distinguished two species, *S. maurus* L. and *S. boehmei*. The latter was described by Kraepelin (1896) from a single female from the shores of Lake Tanganyika. Birula (1910) doubted whether this species belongs to *Scorpio* and did not include it in his revision. Vachon (1950) agreed with Birula and stated that although he had examined a large amount of material from East Africa he had never found *S. boehmei*. Pallary (1938 : 281) recorded a small form of *S. maurus* from the Central Congo. Vachon (1950 : 164, note) rejected this, but the genus does possibly occur in Central Africa. It is now generally accepted that there is only one species in the genus *Scorpio*: *S. maurus*. It is widely distributed from Senegal and Morocco to Egypt and Ethiopia, in the Near East from southern Turkey to Iran and to southern Arabia and India (Birula, 1925).

Scorpio maurus Linnaeus, 1758

Systema Naturae, 10th ed.: p. 624. Type Locality: Africa.

Coloration: Body light yellow to brownish black; walking legs always lighter than body; legs with a dark spot on outer side of base of femur, base of patella and usually

also on base of basitarsus. Body of females usually shining, of males mat. *Size*: About 8 cm long.
Prosoma: Anterior margin with a row of long bristles, a few bristles also on surface; dorsal side smooth, shagreened or with fine granulation laterally; median eyes small, situated in about the middle; distance between eyes variable.
Pectines: With six to 16 denticles; there is overlapping between males and females in the number of denticles.
Pedipalps: Hand with distinct or indistinct crests, these sometimes only indicated by dark lines.
Walking Legs: Sole of tarsi of hind legs with rows of 5–10 spines, at least three of them, usually four or five, situated along latero-apical lobes.

Systematic Remarks: Pocock (1900b) stated that all the forms described are valid species, but at present the various forms are considered to be subspecies of *Scorpio maurus*. Numerous forms and variations have been described, but the characters used for their distinction (coloration, granulation, number of denticles on the pectine and spines on the tarsi, form of the sternal plate of the pectine) show great variation when many specimens of a population are examined. No reliable characters have been found for the distinction of subspecies. We agree with Vachon (1950) that the absence of such characters precludes the distinction of new forms. The following list contains all the forms described, without reference to their validity, apart from those that are generally considered to be synonymous with one of the subspecies.

Scorpio maurus maurus Linnaeus, 1758 : 624	Northern slopes of Algerian and Tunisian mountains; Morocco
Buthus (*Heterometrus*) *palmatus flavus* Hemprich & Ehrenberg, 1829 : 116	
Buthus (*Heterometrus*) *palmatus rufus* Hemprich & Ehrenberg, 1829 : 116	Sinai, southern Israel, Jordan
Buthus (*Heterometrus*) *palmatus fuscus* Hemprich & Ehrenberg, 1829 : 116 (= *Scorpio maurus fuscus*)	Southeastern Turkey, Syria, Lebanon, Israel
Buthus testaceus C.L. Koch, 1839, 5 : 3 (= *Scorpio maurus maurus*)	Coasts of Algeria?
Heterometrus palmatus var. *minor* Simon, 1872, 2 : 258 (= *Scorpio maurus fuscus*)	Lebanon
Heterometrus propinquus Simon, 1872, 2 : 259	Syria (Damascus, ?Palmyra)
Heterometrus maurus var. *berytensis* Simon, 1884, (6) 4 : 192 (= *Scorpio maurus fuscus*)	Lebanon (Beirut, Nahr el-Kalb)
?*Heterometrus boehmei* Kraepelin, 1896, 13 : 131	Shores of Lake Tanganyika
Heterometrus arabicus Pocock, 1900a, (7) 6 : 363	'Arabia'

Heterometrus townsendi Pocock, 1900a, (7)6 : 364	Southwestern Iran (Bushire)
Scorpio maurus magadorensis Birula, 1910, 39 : 147–148	Western Morocco: Agadir to Rabat
Scorpio maurus hesperus Birula, 1910, 39 : 148–151	Northern Morocco: Tangier
Scorpio maurus subtypicus Birula, 1910, 39 : 151–153	Spanish Morocco, Mediterranean coast
Scorpio maurus tunetanus Birula, 1910, 39 : 161–166	Northern Sahara (Tunisia, Algeria and Morocco)
Scorpio maurus kruglovi Birula, 1910, 39 : 180–184	Iraq and Syrian Desert
?Scorpio maurus testaceus Penther, 1912, 26 : 109	Upper Mesopotamia
Heterometrus fuliginosus Pallary, 1928, 34 : 346–348	Morocco (Grand Atlas, 900–2000 m)
Scorpio maurus weidholzi Werner, 1929, 138 : 32–34	Morocco (Marrakesh)
Scorpio maurus legionis Werner, 1932, 141 : 289	Morocco (Grand Atlas)
Scorpio maurus yemenensis Werner, 1936, 2 : 183–184	Yemen
Scorpio maurus occidentalis Werner, 1936, 2 : 184–185	Senegal, north to Upper Gambia
?Heterometrus maurus ssp. Pallary, 1938, 16(3) : 281	Central Congo
Scorpio maurus behringsi Schenkel, 1949, 60 : 193	Morocco
Scorpio maurus stemmleri Schenkel, 1949, 60 : 194	Morocco (Demnat)

There is a dark subspecies, *S. m. fuscus,* in north and central Israel, and a light subspecies, *S. m. palmatus*, occurring in southern Israel and Sinai. There is almost no character by which the two subspecies may be distinguished except the colour. The two subspecies are closely related, almost identical morphologically. However, there are always specimens of only one colour in the range of each form. In peripheral populations specimens of both colours occur together and many individuals are of mixed colour, thus forming intermediate populations of the same species.

Hemprich & Ehrenberg (1829) distinguished two variations of different shading among the light-coloured specimens. *Scorpio m. palmatus flavus* was described from Lower Egypt and the coastal plain of Libya, *S. m. palmatus rufus* from the Sinai mountains and the coastal plain of Sinai near Et-Tur. Specimens from Sinai and southern Israel were compared but no differences in colour were found. Material from the range of *flavus* has been examined and this variation is apparently not a valid form. The differences between the two subspecies *fuscus* and *palmatus* are minor and do not justify the distinction of variations of *palmatus* alone.

Simon (1872) described the subspecies *propinquus* from Damascus and also recorded it from Naplouse (*leg.* Brulerie). Study of Simon's old atlas and the diary of Brulerie (1875) proved that Naplouse stands, as Pocock (1900a) suggested, for Nablus (= Shechem) in Samaria. Birula (1910) wrongly rejected Pocock's interpretation of Nablus, but was apparently correct in stating that it was unlikely that this desert form would occur in Nablus. Furthermore, *S. m. fuscus* occurs in Nablus and two so closely related subspecies could not exist separately in the same area. Later Simon always mentioned *propinquus* only from Damascus. We agree with Birula that *S. m. propinquus* should not be considered to occur in our area.

Key to the Subspecies of Scorpio maurus in Israel and Sinai
(Map 8)

1. Genital operculum almost always longer than sternum in females, often as long as sternum in males; vesicule often slightly wider than fifth segment; coloration light olive-brown to yellow; southern Israel and Sinai. **S. maurus palmatus**
– Genital operculum distinctly longer than sternum in both sexes; vesicule usually narrower than fifth segment; coloration dark brown to greenish black; central and northern Israel. **S. maurus fuscus**

Note: Characters of the subspecies of *S. maurus* are less distinct or partly absent at the periphery of its range.

Scorpio maurus palmatus (Hemprich & Ehrenberg, 1829)
Figs. 91–95; Map 8

Buthus (*Heterometrus*) *palmatus rufus* Hemprich & Ehrenberg, 1829, *Berolini ex officina Academica* : 116. Type Locality: Sinai.
Buthus (*Heterometrus*) *palmatus flavus* Hemprich & Ehrenberg, 1829, *Berolini ex officina Academica* : 116. Type Localities: Egypt and Libya.
Heterometrus maurus—. Simon, 1892, *Revue Biol. Nord. Fr.* (*Lille*), 5 : 84.
Heterometrus palmatus—. Pocock, 1900, *Ann. Mag. Nat. Hist. Lond.*, (7)6 : 363.
Scorpio palmatus—. Birula, 1908, *Sber. Akad. Wiss. Wien,* 117 : 147.
Scorpio maurus palmatus—. Birula, 1910, *Horae Soc. Ent. Ross.*, 39 : 166–169.

Coloration: Light olive-brown to yellow; fifth segment of metasoma alone or together with stinger sometimes slightly darker; pedipalps of same colour as body or slightly darker, but fingers always dark brown to black; legs yellow, with a dark spot at base of femur, patella and basitarsus.
Prosoma: Smooth, only slightly shagreened laterally and posteriorly in females; in males, surface shagreened, but not granulate, with smooth areas sometimes anteriorly; sternum wider than long.
Mesosoma: Tergites 1–6 shining and smooth, at most slightly shagreened laterally in females, mat and slightly shagreened in males; seventh tergite of females usually smooth anteriorly, shagreened or granulate posteriorly and laterally, crests granulate and present only in posterior half of segment; whole seventh tergite shagreened and granulate in males, and crests distinct; posterior margin of tergites with short hairs and a long bristle on seventh tergite at end of each crest; genital operculum almost always longer than sternum in females, often as long as sternum in males; sternites 3–6 smooth and shining in females, shining but finely reticulate in males; seventh

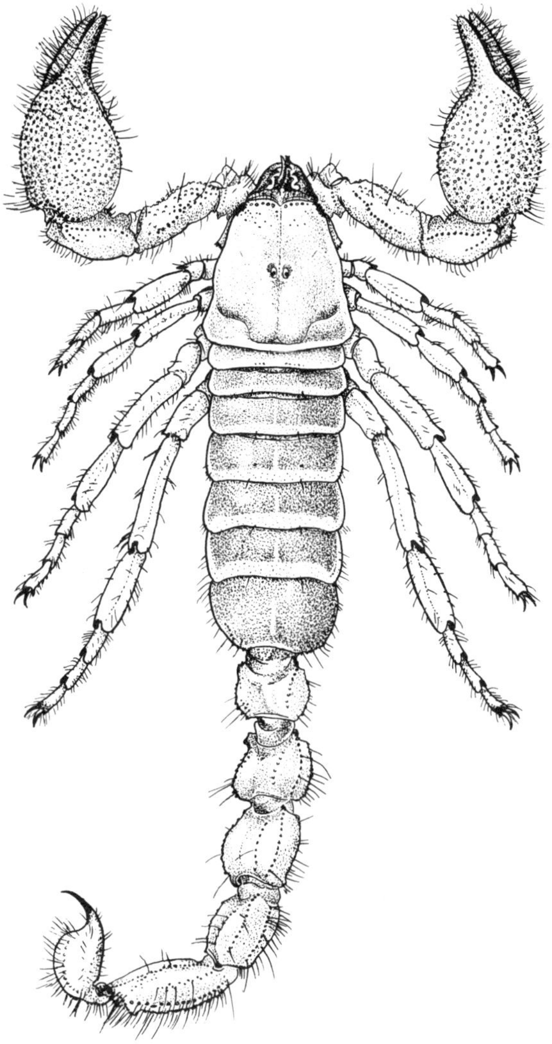

Fig. 91: *Scorpio maurus palmatus* (Hemprich & Ehrenberg, 1829)
Male from Jericho, Israel (Sc. 988); total length 55 mm

sternite rugose with four tuberculate crests, crests sometimes almost smooth and indistinct.

Metasoma: In females dorsal side of first segment usually slightly granulate, mainly between dorsal and latero-dorsal crests, other segments smooth or almost smooth; in males, all segments on the dorsal side shagreened and with small granules which become sparser posteriorly; dorsal crests of segments 1–4 with small, spaced granules; in females segments 1–2 slightly granulate laterally, other segments smooth; in males 1–3 shagreened laterally and with small granules, fourth segment almost smooth, fifth segment granulate only in anterior half; latero-ventral crests of females in the form of distinctly raised lines on segments 1–3, only slightly indicated on

92

93

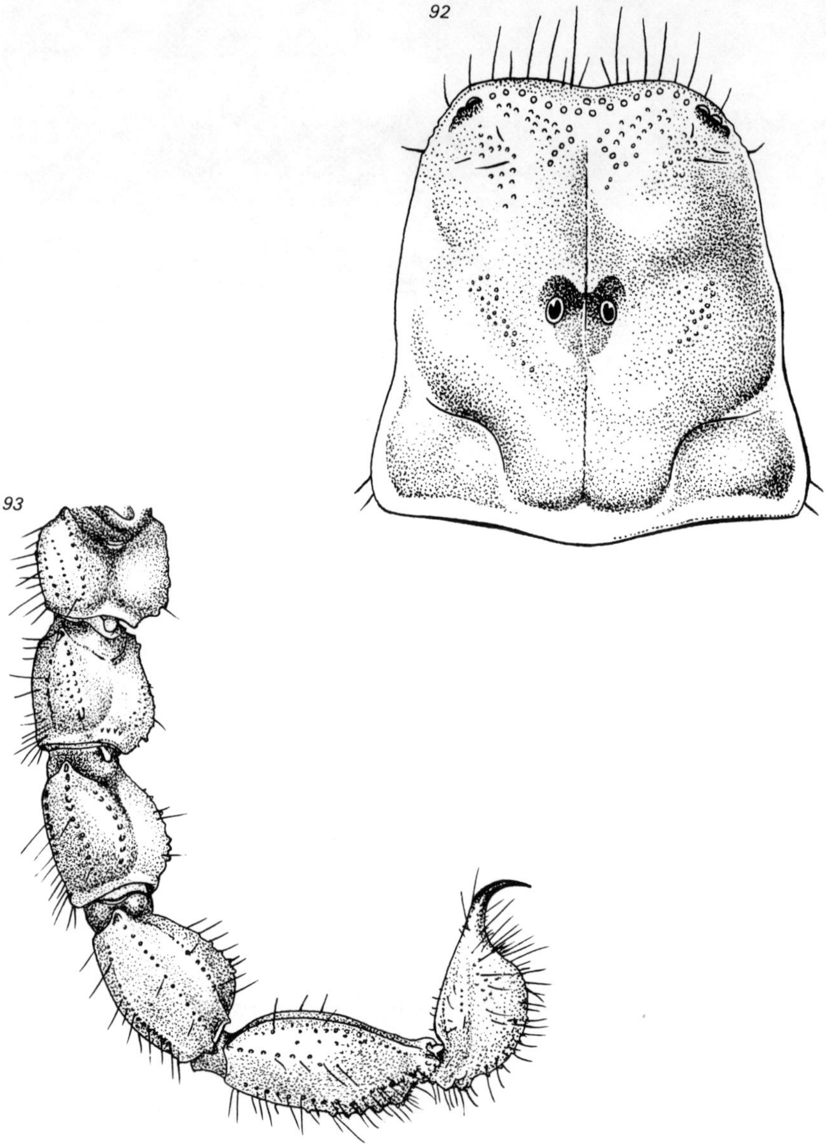

Figs. 92–93: *Scorpio maurus palmatus* (Hemprich & Ehrenberg, 1829)
92. prosoma, length 8.0 mm; 93. metasoma, length 30 mm

segment 4; latero-ventral crests of males in the form of raised lines on segments 1–2, smooth and only slightly indicated on segments 3–4; in both sexes granules of latero-ventral crests on fifth segment small and separate anteriorly, in the form of large, separate cones on posterior part; first segment and sometimes also second segment

94

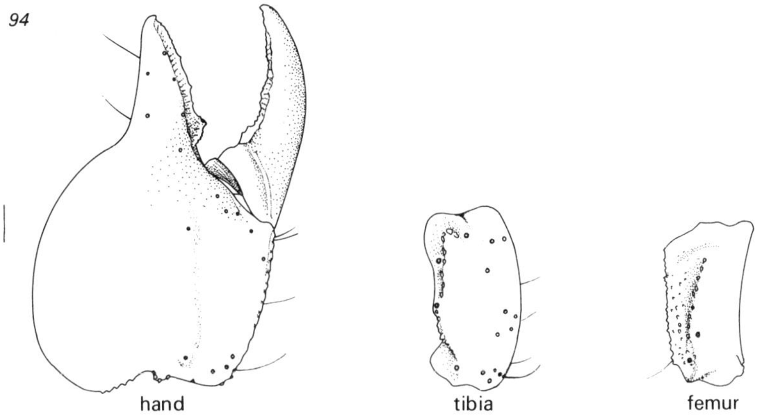

95

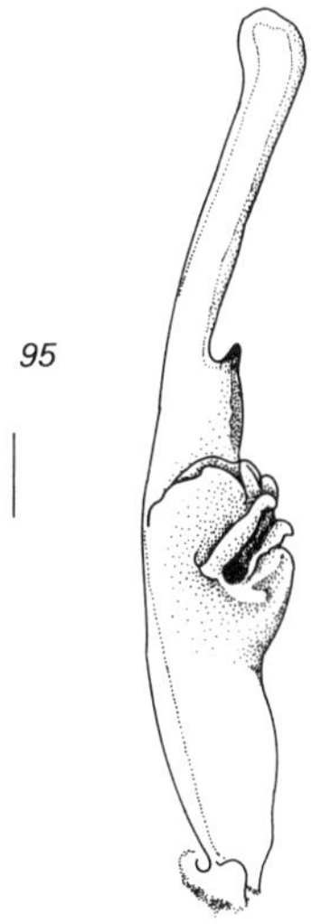

Figs. 94–95: *Scorpio maurus palmatus* (Hemprich & Ehrenberg, 1829)
94. pedipalp, arrangement of trichobothria; 95. paraxial organ; scale-lines 1 mm

with a short, oblique intermediary crest, segments 3–4 without intermediary crests, fifth segment with distinct intermediary crests in anterior half of segment or slightly more, with fused granules in females, separate granules in males; segments smooth ventrally except for slight granulation at base of first segment, at most slightly shagreened near margin in males; ventral crests of segments 1–2 markedly raised and tuberculate, crests flat and smooth on segments 3–4, sometimes only indicated, crests with distinct, separate granules on fifth segment; axial crest of fifth segment granulate and bifurcate distally; lateral anal lobes of fifth segment consisting of continuation of granules of latero-ventral crests; all segments and vesicule with many bristles; vesicule smooth dorsally, with longitudinal granulate crests ventrally; vesicule often slightly wider than fifth segment.

Pectines: Extending to coxo-trochanteral articulation of leg IV in both sexes, sometimes beyond articulation in males; females with 7–13 (usually 9–12) denticles, males with 9–13 (usually 10–13) denticles.

Pedipalps: Femur with bristles, with large granules on inner side; dorsal outer crest with distinct, separate granules distally, sometimes with several rows of granules; femur of female smooth ventrally and on outer side, of male shagreened with fine granulation; median-dorsal crest of tibia with distinct, dark, fused granules; inner-ventral crest with only 4–5 dark spots in females, longer and with separate granules in males; tibia with bristles, smooth or at most slightly tuberculate dorsally in females, only ventrally smooth, shagreened laterally and distinctly granulate dorsally in males; hand with many bristles, smooth on outer side and ventrally on proximal part, granulate on distal third and reticulate dorsally with low ridges mixed with granules and tubercles; dorsal crests usually distinct, ventral-outer crest in the form of a smooth, raised, dark line; movable finger distinctly longer than hand and without recess at base.

Walking Legs: Basitarsus of leg IV with about five spines near spur ventrally on outer side; each row of spines on sole of tarsus of leg IV with 6–10 (usually 7–10) spines.

Measurements (mm): *Female*. Adult, 'Arad (No. Sc. 1213). Total length 74; prosoma 11, mesosoma 26, metasoma 37. Segments of metasoma: first L3.1, W5.3, H4.0; second 3.6–4.8–3.8; third 4.1–4.8–3.6; fourth 5.1–4.4–3.7; fifth 6.5–4.0–3.5. Stinger (pedicel + vesicule + aculeus) L8.8; vesicule W4.3. Pedipalps: femur L6.7, W3.5; tibia L7.5, W3.7; hand L7.0, maximum W10.4; movable finger L10.5. Number of denticles of pectine 11–11.

Male. Adult, 'Arad (No. Sc. 1239). Total length 63; prosoma 9, mesosoma 22, metasoma 32. Segments of metasoma: first L2.8, W4.5, H3.4; second 3.4–4.3–3.4; third 3.8–4.1–3.4; fourth 4.7–3.8–3.2; fifth 5.8–3.3–3.0. Stinger (pedicel + vesicule + aculeus) L7.8; vesicule W3.4. Pedipalps: femur L5.9, W3.0; tibia L6.3, W3.3; hand L.5.7; maximum W8.8; movable finger L9.0. Number of denticles of pectine 12–12.

Distribution: The references of the following records are summarized in the Appendix on Distribution. Coastal plain of Libyan Desert: Cyrenaica. Lower Egypt: Alexandria, Wadi Natrun, Cairo, Faiyum. Jordan: As-Salt; new record from the Hebrew University: Wadi Deba' 100 km southeast of Amman.

Israel and Sinai (Map 8): *Scorpio maurus palmatus* occurs in northern and central Sinai and in southern Israel to the foothills of Judea. It extends north along the Judean Desert to Jericho, and to about 25 km southeast of Tel Aviv (Birula, 1910, records 'En Gedi for *S. m. fuscus*, but only *S. m. palmatus* occurs there). *Scorpio m. palmatus* is probably absent in the Coastal Plain, as well as in the sand dunes of northern Sinai.

Ecological Notes: *Scorpio maurus palmatus* is very common. It is found on brown-red sandy soils, loess and alluvial soils and in stony desert. It burrows and can move stones heavier than itself. Each scorpion lives alone in a burrow, but concentrations of hundreds of burrows may be found in certain areas. The burrow has a crescent-

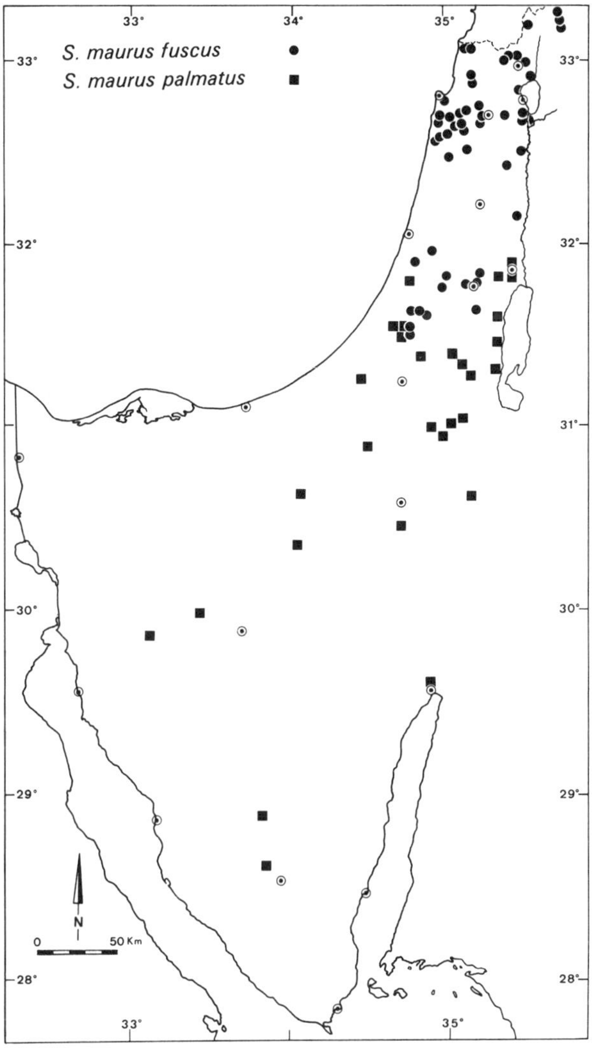

Map 8: Records of *Scorpio* in Israel and Sinai

shaped opening and runs fairly parallel to the ground for about 10 cm, after which it turns downwards for 20 to 70 cm. The bottom of the burrow is slightly enlarged. The animal leaves the burrow at night or stands at the entrance with the pincers slightly raised. It is rather agile. Males have been observed (Rosin & Shulov, 1961) to produce sounds by rapidly striking the posterior half of the mesosoma against the ground. Parturition in August–September; number of young 8–13. *Scorpio m. palmatus* preys on small and large arthropods. It does not sting readily, and the sting is not very painful.

Scorpio maurus fuscus (Hemprich & Ehrenberg, 1829)

Figs. 96–98; Map 8

Buthus (*Heterometrus*) *palmatus fuscus* Hemprich & Ehrenberg, 1829, *Berolini ex officina Academica* : 116. Type Locality: Beirut, Lebanon.

Heterometrus palmatus var. *minor* Simon, 1872, *Annls Soc. Ent. Fr.,* (5)2 : 258. Type Locality: Lebanon.

Heterometrus maurus var. *berytensis* Simon, 1884, *Annls Soc. Ent. Fr.,* (6)4 : 192. Type Locality: Beirut, Nahr el-Kalb, Lebanon; type in the Muséum National, Paris; examined.

Scorpio testaceus (C.L. Koch, 1839).Kraepelin, 1899, *Das Tierreich,* 8. Lief., Berlin: 125 (misdetermination).

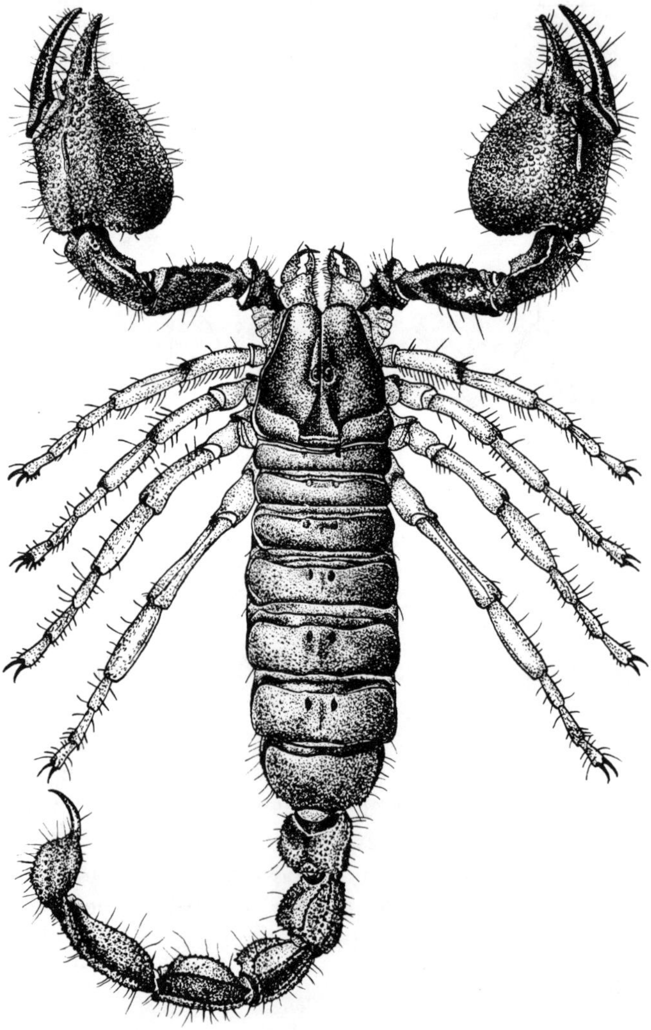

Fig. 96: *Scorpio maurus fuscus* (Hemprich & Ehrenberg, 1829)
Male from HaSolelim, Israel (Sc. 1619); total length 62 mm

Scorpio palmatus—. Birula, 1900, Moscou, *Izv. Obshch. Lyub. Estestv.*, 98(3) : 13.
Heterometrus fuscus—. Pocock, 1900, *Ann. Mag. Nat. Hist. Lond.*, (7)6 : 363.
Scorpio fuscus—. Werner, 1902, *Verh. Zool.-Bot. Ges. Wien*, 52 : 602.
Scorpio maurus fuscus—. Birula, 1910, *Horae Soc. Ent. Ross.*, 39 : 173–178.

Coloration: Dark brown to greenish black; proximal part of legs and pectines light ventrally; pedipalps of same colour as body, fingers always black; legs olive-brown to brown, with slightly dark, sometimes indistinct spot at base of femur, patella and basitarsus.
Prosoma: As in *S. m. palmatus*, but surface shagreened and with small granules in males.
Mesosoma: As in *S. m. palmatus*, but surface of tergites and crests usually with denser and coarser granules; genital operculum distinctly longer than sternum in both sexes; sternites with many bristles.
Metasoma: As above, segments and crests more granulate than in *S. m. palmatus*, sometimes with pointed granules in males; vesicule usually narrower than fifth segment.
Pectines: Females with 6–10 (usually 8–10) denticles, males with 9–11 (usually also 9–11) denticles.
Pedipalps: Tibia smooth, shagreened only on inner side or with small granules in both sexes; dorsal crests of hand usually indistinct.
Measurements (*mm*): *Female*. Adult, Ḫadid, near Ben Shemen (No. Sc. 1553). Total length 70; prosoma 10, mesosoma 26, metasoma 34. Segments of metasoma: first

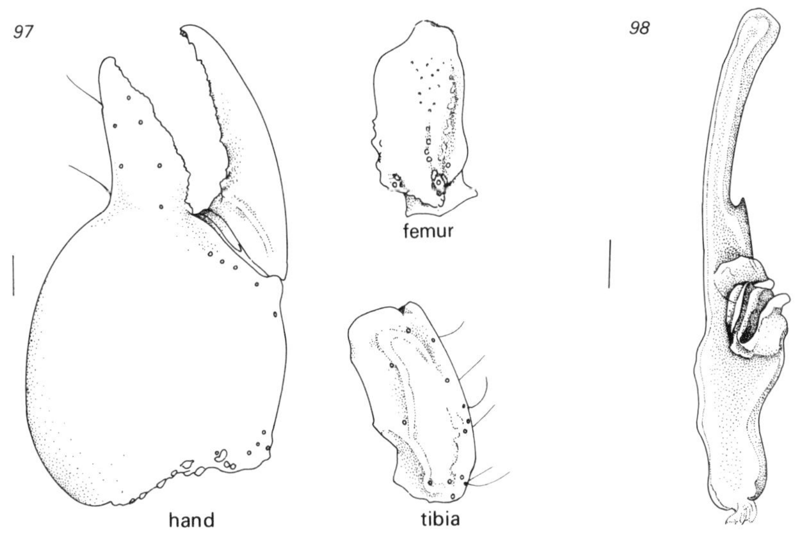

Figs. 97–98: *Scorpio maurus fuscus* (Hemprich & Ehrenberg, 1829)
97. pedipalp, arrangement of trichobothria; 98. paraxial organ; scale-lines 1 mm

L2.7, W5.1, H3.7; second 3.5–4.5–3.7; third 3.8–4.4–3.8; fourth 4.6–4.0–3.7; fifth 5.7–3.5–3.2. Stinger (pedicel + vesicule + aculeus) L7.5; vesicule W3.2. Pedipalps: femur L6.2, W3.4; tibia L7.3, W3.2; hand L6.4, maximum W8.7; movable finger L9.3. Number of denticles of pectine 10–10.

Male. Adult, Ḫadid, near Ben Shemen (No. Sc. 1564). Total length 58; prosoma 9, mesosoma 17, metasoma 32. Segments of metasoma: first L2.7, W4.5, H3.4; second 3.4–4.1–3.3; third 3.8–4.0–3.7; fourth 4.2–3.7–3.6; fifth 5.7–3.2–3.1. Stinger (pedicel + vesicule + aculeus) L7.4; vesicule W2.7. Pedipalps: femur L5.7, W3.2; tibia L6.6, W3.4; hand L.6.0, maximum W8.4; movable finger L8.6. Number of denticles of pectine 10–10.

Distribution: The references of the following records are summarized in the Appendix on Distribution. Southeast Turkey: From Elazig to Mersin and to the Amanus Mt. Syria: Latakieh, Djéroud (60 km northeast of Damascus). Lebanon: 'En Zahalte, Beirut, Nahr-el-Kalb.

Israel (Map 8; p. 111): *Scorpio maurus fuscus* occurs in Israel from the north to the Judean Mountains and along the Jordan Valley to about Jiftlik, 40 km south of Bet She'an. It is absent in a narrow zone along the Coastal Plain.

Ecological Notes: *Scorpio maurus fuscus* is fairly common. It is found on terra rossa, basalt, rendzina and brown-red sandy soils. Although it is a burrowing form, it is occasionally found under stones without a burrow. Dense concentrations of burrows are not usual. The burrow has a crescent-shaped opening and generally runs vertical, without turns, to a depth of about 40 cm. An agile form which does not sting readily but snaps rapidly with its pincers, it can be kept in large numbers in containers usually without cannibalism. As in *S. m. palmatus,* the males are known to produce sounds. Parturition usually in August–September; number of young 11–16. It preys on small and large arthropods.

Family DIPLOCENTRIDAE Pocock, 1893

Diplocentrini Pocock, 1893, *Ann. Mag. Nat. Hist. Lond.*, (6) 12 : 307

Type Genus: *Diplocentrus* Peters, 1861.
Diagnosis: Sternum pentagonal; legs with only one outer basitarsal spur; aculeus with subaculear tubercle at base.

The Diplocentridae include two subfamilies, the Neotropic Diplocentrinae and the Nebinae of the Old World. The Nebinae include two genera: *Nebo* Simon, 1878, with one species (*N. hierichonticus*), and *Heteronebo* Pocock, 1899, from the island of Abd-el-Kuri (near Socotra), with two species (*H. granti* and *H. forbesi*). According to Pocock (1894), Kraepelin (1905) and Birula (1917 : 134), the Nebinae are a relict of a Palaearctic fauna of scorpions that was driven south.

Genus NEBO Simon, 1878

Annls Soc. Ent. Fr., (5) 8 : 399

Type Species: *Hemiscorpio hierichonticus* Simon, 1872.

Diagnosis: Prosoma divided dorsally by a deep median groove; tarsi of legs with rounded latero-apical lobes.

Prosoma: Anterior margin deeply incised in the middle; crests absent; deep transverse groove passing along posterior margin and joining median groove in the middle; median eyes small, situated anterior to middle; three lateral eyes distinct; sternum deeply incised in middle of posterior margin.
Mesosoma: Tergites smooth, shagreened or with fine granulation; all tergites except seventh without crests; genital operculum divided medially into two plates in males, only indented medially in females; seventh sternite with four straight crests.
Metasoma: Relatively long and slender; segments smooth, shagreened or with fine granulation; crests smooth, granulate or with fused granules; vesicule flat and smooth dorsally, globular and granulate ventrally; aculeus very short.
Pectines: Sternal plate with slightly concave anterior margin and straight posterior margin; pectines extending to or beyond coxo-trochanteral articulation of leg IV; outer side with hairs and inner fulcra with one fine hair or bristle.
Chelicerae: Immovable finger with three teeth on inner side, without teeth ventrally, and with two long bristles dorsally; movable finger with three teeth dorsally, without teeth ventrally.
Pedipalps: Femur and tibia with distinct crests; hand thick and broad; fingers thick, curved, with or without a large recess at base.
Walking Legs: Sole of tarsi with short spines in two rows extending to narrow latero-apical lobes near claws; tarsi with a small dorsal finger-like process apically between claws; claws short and curved.

Review of Genus: Simon (1872) described a new species, *hierichonticus*, based on two specimens from Jericho in the Jordan Valley, and placed it in the genus *Hemiscorpio* Peters, 1861 (Scorpionidae). Simon (1878) established, for this species, the genus *Nebo*.

Nebo flavipes was described by Simon (1882) from Yemen (Ta'izz). Simon added that it was also collected by Letourneux at Mar Saba, 'Syria' (doubtless the Monastery of Mar Saba, east of Bethlehem). Kraepelin (1899) was doubtful about this species and thought that Simon had the male of *N. hierichonticus*. Pocock (1895) and Birula (1910, 1917) mentioned *N. flavipes* as a valid species. Werner (1934) at first omitted it from the genus, but mentioned it again in 1935 as a valid species. Whittick (1941) synonymized *N. flavipes* with *N. hierichonticus*. Rosin & Shulov (1963) examined many specimens of *N. hierichonticus* from Israel and found only one species in Israel. Vachon (1965, 1965–1966) re-examined the specimens of Simon from Yemen and Israel and considered *N. flavipes* a synonym of *N. hierichonticus*. This has been confirmed by examination of numerous specimens from the entire distribution range. Pocock (1903) described the subspecies *N. h. pallidimanus* from Yemen. After studying specimens from Arabia, we consider *pallidimanus* as a pale colour variation, and no distinct range of distribution can be defined.

Kraepelin (1899) introduced the misspelling *hierochonticus*, which was used for a long time.

Substantiated records of the distribution of *N. hierichonticus* are only from Israel, Sinai, Jordan and Arabia. Syria has been mentioned by all authors since Simon (1878), but no localities in this country have been published. This species may occur in Syria and Lebanon. Simon (1910) recorded it from Egypt, near Suez and Cairo. There is only one specimen, possibly from Gebel Ataka, Egypt, in Simon's collection, and there are no other records from Egypt in the collections examined.

Nebo hierichonticus (Simon, 1872)

Figs. 99–103; Map 9

Hemiscorpio hierichonticus Simon, 1872, *Annls Soc. Ent. Fr.*, (5)2 : 255–257. Type Locality: Jordan Valley, Israel; type in the Muséum National, Paris; examined.

Nebo hierichonticus—. Simon, 1878, *Annls Soc. Ent. Fr.*, (5)8 : 399–400.

Nebo flavipes Simon, 1882, *Annali Mus. Civ. Stor. Nat. Genova*, 18 : 249–250. Type Locality: Ta'izz, Yemen; type in the Muséum National, Paris; examined.

Nebo hierochonticus—. Kraepelin, 1899, *Das Tierreich*, 8. Lief., Berlin: 98.

Nebo hierichonticus pallidimanus Pocock, 1903, *Ann. Mag. Nat. Hist. Lond.*, (7)11 : 214. Type Localities: El Kubar and Gerba, Yemen.

Coloration: Body and pedipalps olive-brown, reddish brown, dark brown to black; sternites and pectines yellowish olive, legs light brown to yellowish olive. Body of females usually shining, of males mat. *Size*: Adult females may be over 13 cm long. *Prosoma*: About as long as wide at posterior margin; smooth in the middle, shagreened and with small granules laterally in females; in males, almost entire surface densely shagreened and with small granules laterally; median tubercle of eyes usually

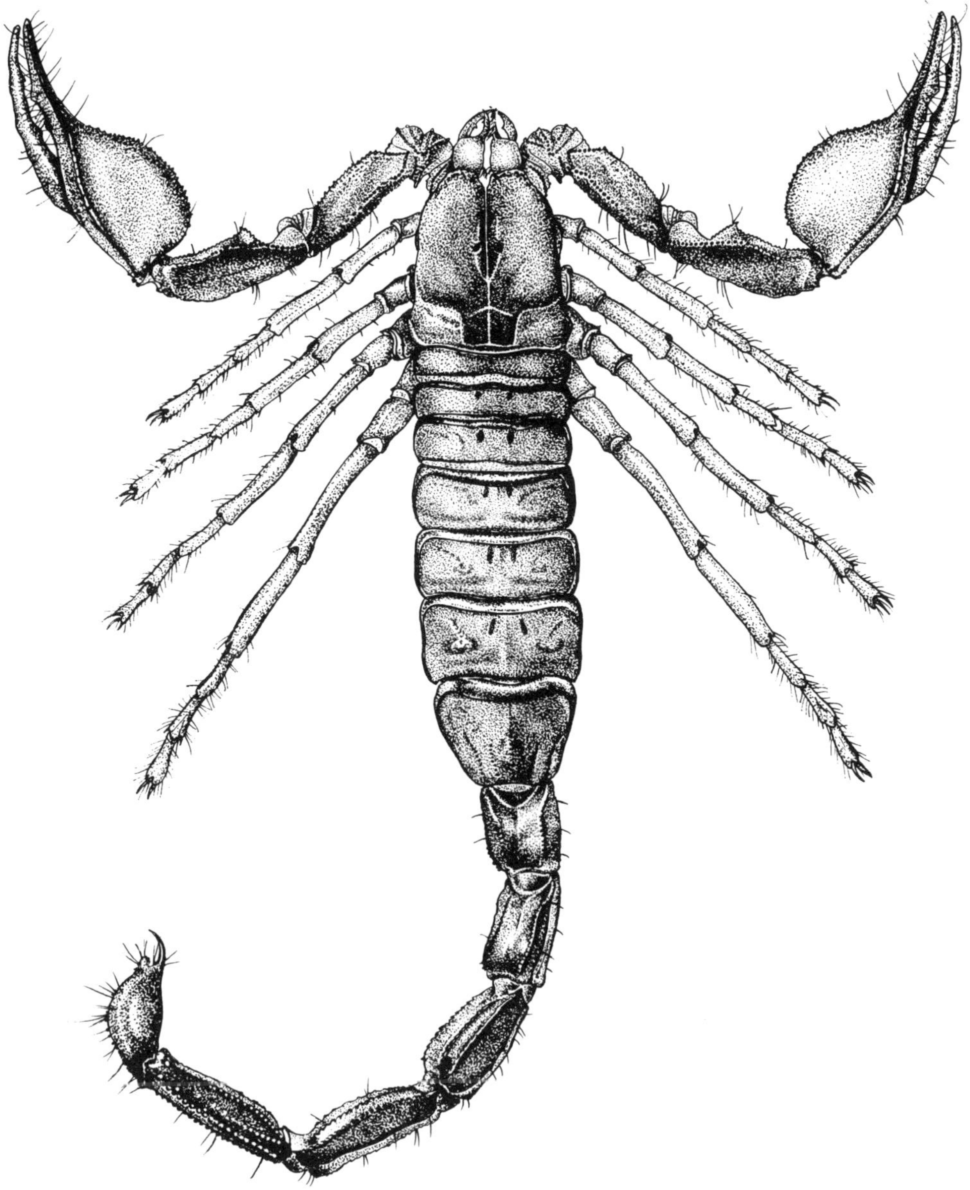

Fig. 99: *Nebo hierichonticus* (Simon, 1872)
Male from Umm el Faḫm, Israel (Sc. 2204); total length 87 mm

smooth, sometimes (in males) with a few granules on both sides of the median groove before and behind the tubercle; median eyes separated from each other by more than their diameter; lateral eyes arranged in a slight curve, anterior eyes slightly larger and closer to each other than to smaller posterior eye; posterior margin of prosoma almost straight; anterior margin with a row of long bristles, a few bristles also on surface, two bristles situated behind median eyes.

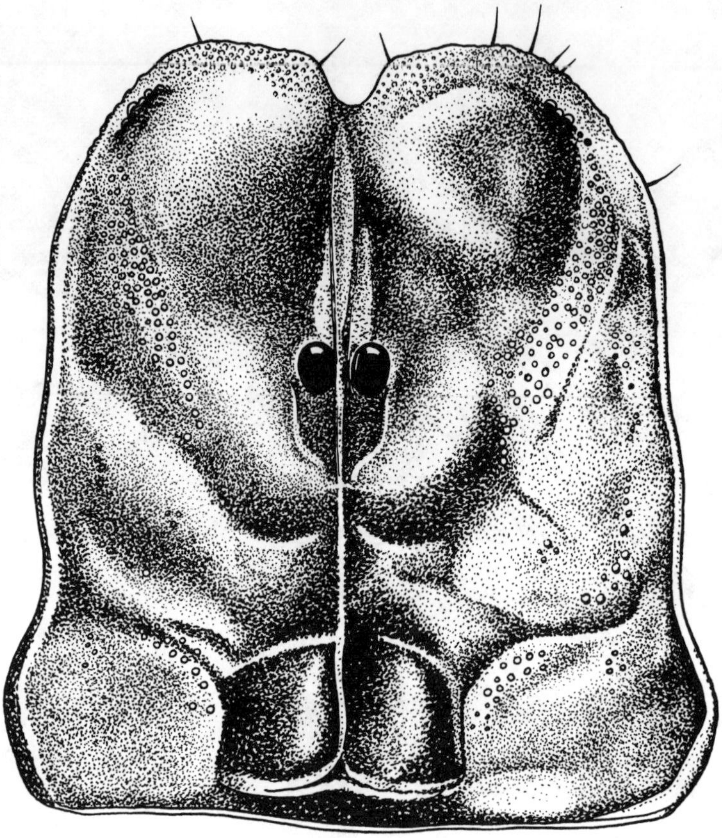

Fig. 100: *Nebo hierichonticus* (Simon, 1872). Prosoma, length 9.7 mm

Mesosoma: Tergites 1–6 shining, smooth, sometimes slightly shagreened on anterior tergites laterally in females, mat and densely shagreened throughout in males; seventh tergite with four distinct crests in posterior half, inner pair of crests sometimes indistinct in females; seventh tergite densely shagreened in males, usually only slightly shagreened, mainly near crests, in females; posterior margin of tergites with a few short hairs; sternites smooth and shining, only seventh sternite slightly shagreened laterally in males; seventh sternite with two or four smooth crests which are sometimes only slightly indicated; sternites with bristles.

Metasoma: All segments distinctly longer than wide or high; anterior segments smooth or slightly shagreened dorsally in females, posterior segments sometimes with a few small granules; anterior segments coarsely and densely shagreened and with small granules which decrease posteriorly in size in males; dorsal crests of first segment smooth in females, with fused or slightly separate granules in males; dorsal crests of segments 2–4 with slightly separate granules mainly in posterior part of crests; segments smooth laterally in females, at most slightly shagreened on posterior segments; sides slightly shagreened, less distinctly on posterior segments in males; latero-dorsal and latero-ventral crests smooth on segments 1–4, latero-dorsal crests

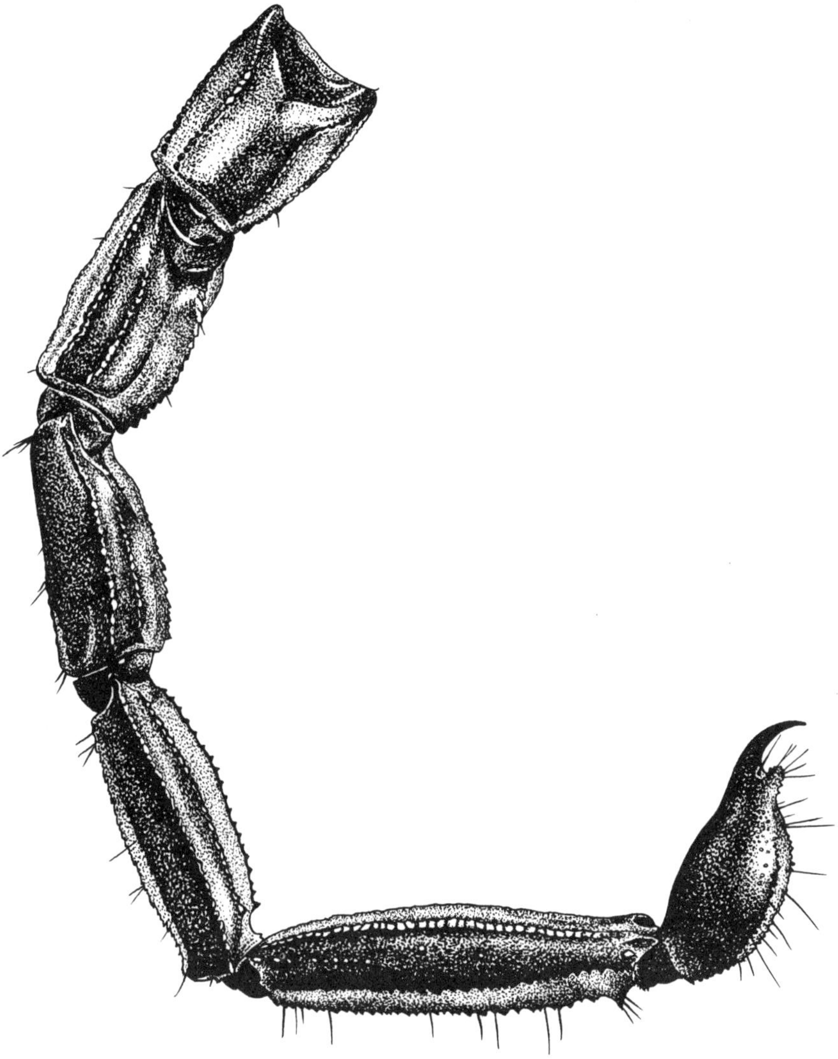

Fig. 101: *Nebo hierichonticus* (Simon, 1872). Metasoma, length 49 mm

of males sometimes with fused granules; latero-dorsal crests of fifth segment consisting of several rows of small pointed granules, and latero-ventral crests consisting of distinct teeth; first segment with complete intermediary crests which are usually smooth; intermediary crests of segments 2–4 absent or slightly indicated by small granules, mainly on second segment; intermediary crest of fifth segment distinct, with fused or separate granules, extending over two thirds or more of anterior part of segment; all segments smooth ventrally, sometimes slightly shagreened on posterior part of segments 2–4 in males; ventral crests of segments 1 and 2, and usually also of segment 3, smooth, sometimes with fused granules on posterior part of third segment; ventral crests of segment 4 with fused granules, or sometimes with separate

102

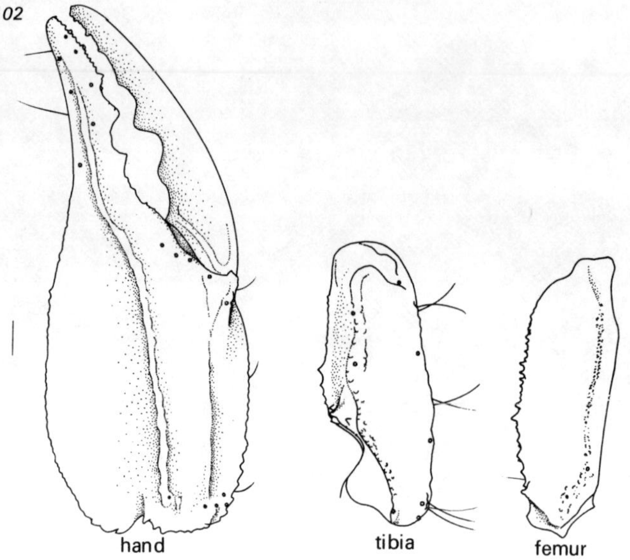

103

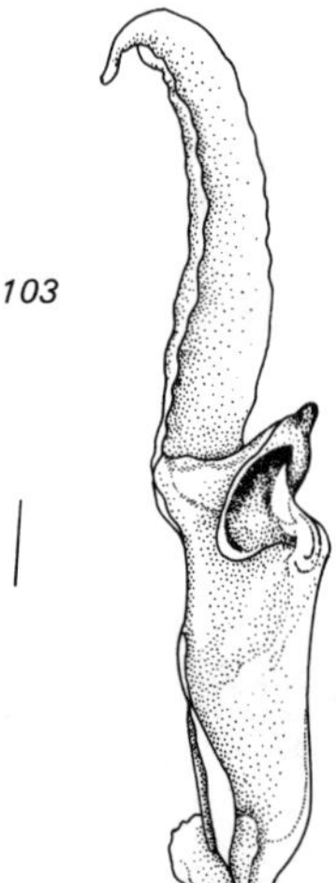

Figs. 102–103: *Nebo hierichonticus* (Simon; 1872)
102. pedipalp, arrangement of trichobothria; 103. paraxial organ; scale-lines 1 mm

granules in males; axial crest of fifth segment markedly raised and with relatively large, pointed granules; crest usually slightly bifurcate distally; ventral crests with at most a few granules in posterior part of segment; all segments and stinger with bristles; vesicule sometimes longer than three-quarters of fifth segment and distinctly wider than this segment; vesicule 5–6 times longer than aculeus; aculeus curved, with large, granulate subaculear tubercle bearing many hairs.

Pectines: Females with 11–17 (usually 13–15) denticles, males with 14–22 (usually 16–18) denticles.
Pedipalps: Femur with distinctly granulate crests, distinctly more than twice as long as wide, densely granulate dorsally, ventrally and on inner side, without outer accessory bristles; tibia with distinct pedicular tubercles and crests; most crests smooth or with fused granules, but median-dorsal crests with large, rounded, separate granules; tibia more than twice as long as wide, almost smooth ventrally, shagreened or with small granules dorsally and on outer side, inner side granulate, without outer accessory bristles; hand large, only slightly longer than wide, flat dorsally; dorsal-inner crest consisting of several rows of large granules; ventral and outer-dorsal crests smooth; short crests of 2–5 granules at base, laterally; inner side of hand granulate, reticulate and slightly shagreened dorsally, outer side smooth; fingers longer than prosoma and distinctly longer than hand; fingers of females with a large recess at base; denticles of movable finger mixed with groups of coarse granules, but denticles sometimes arranged in a continuous line along the finger.
Walking Legs: Basitarsus of all legs with 4–6 spines near spur ventrally on outer side and another spine more proximally; each row of spines on sole of tarsus of leg IV with 6–10 spines.
Measurements (mm): *Female*. Adult, Mash'abbe Sade (No. Sc. 1298). Total length 126; prosoma 14, mesosoma 46, metasoma 66. Segments of metasoma: first L7.4, W5.8, H4.6; second 8.4–5.3–4.2; third 9.5–4.9–4.1; fourth 10.5–4.5–4.0; fifth 14.0–4.0–4.0. Vesicule (including pedicel) L9.8, W5.0; aculeus L1.8. Pedipalps: femur L12.0, W4.6; tibia L11.2, W5.0; hand L10.4, W10.0; movable finger L14.5. Number of denticles of pectine 14–14.
Male. Adult, Jerusalem (No. Sc. 915). Total length 96; prosoma 11, mesosoma 30, metasoma 55. Segments of metasoma: first L6.3, W5.0, H4.0; second 7.3–4.4–3.9; third 8.0–4.3–3.8; fourth 9.0–3.9–3.6; fifth 11.4–3.5–3.5. Vesicule (including pedicel) L8.4, W4.4; aculeus L1.6. Pedipalps: femur L10.7, W4.0; tibia L10.0, W4.1; hand L9.3, W8.0; movable finger L13.4. Number of denticles of pectine 17–18.
Distribution: The references of the following records are summarized in the Appendix on Distribution. ?Egypt: Gebel Ataka near Suez, Gebel Mokattam near Cairo (records need substantiation). Arabia: Dibba, Muscat, Qara Mt., Hadhramaut, Yemen, Aden. Jordan: Amman, Petra (records from the British Museum).
Israel and Sinai (Map 9): *Nebo hierichonticus* is found from the north throughout Israel to southern Sinai. It is absent in the Coastal Plain from about south of the Carmel ridge to northern Sinai. The species is recorded here for the first time from Sinai.
Ecological Notes: *Nebo hierichonticus*, the largest scorpion in our country, is quite common. It is found on terra rossa, basalt and rendzina soil and in stony desert. It digs burrows but is also found under large stones, in rock crevices and in empty rodent burrows. The burrow runs parallel or slightly oblique to the surface, to a depth of 20–40 cm. Parturition mainly in September; number of young 30–45. It moves rather slowly and preys on large arthropods. The sting is mildly painful and produces local haemorrhages and slight necrosis.

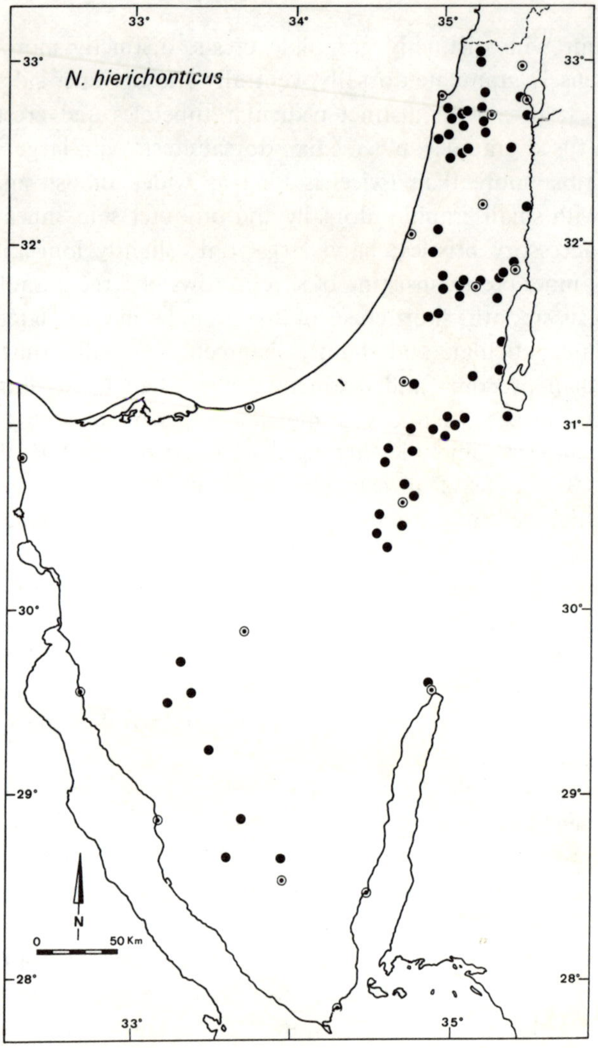

Map 9: Records of *Nebo* in Israel and Sinai

APP

Distribution of Scorpi

The numbers listed herein refer to previous records given in the Referenc

	Egypt	Sinai	Israel	Jordan
Androctonus amoreuxi hebraeus		†	87,90,96	
A. australis	in large parts of N. Africa	30,31,79		
A. bicolor bicolor	?1*,9,14,27,54, 77,79,87,90,95	30,31	27,90,95,96	
A. crassicauda crassicauda		†	4,8,11,14,51,64,67 74,90,96,100	11,14,90; new records Amman, Qasr Amra
Buthacus arenicola	44–near Suez Canal; populations dispersed in northern Africa	44		
B. leptochelys leptochelys	in large parts of N. Africa	30,31,44	44, ?74 (all records listed are doubtful)	?Wadi Deba‘
B. leptochelys nitzani			44	
B. yotvatensis			44	
Buthotus judaicus			4,38,46,60,64,74, 93,96	51–Jarash
Buthus occitanus israelis	?*	38	38,65	
Compsobuthus carmelitis			44	
C. longipalpis		44	44	
C. werneri judaicus			8,9,11,14,44,90,96,100	
C. werneri werneri	in large parts of northern Africa	44	44	
Leirus quinquestriatus hebraeus		30,31,38 41,43,77, 95	recorded by all authors	43–Mafrak, 64–Petra; new record–Wadi Deb
Nebo hierichonticus	?(27,73–Gebel Ataka, 77–Gebel Mokattam)*	†	4,11,14,41,51,63,67, 70,73,74,88,90,93, 96,100	Amman, Petra
Orthochirus scrobiculosus negebensis		†	34,66,74	near Amman, Qasr Amra
Scorpio maurus fuscus			8,11,14,41,55, 74,90,96,100	
S. maurus palmatus	9–Wadi Natrun; 11, 14,27–Cairo, 30,31, 55,77–Alexandria, Faiyum; 90	30,31	11,27,51,74,90,96	51–As Salt, 96; new record–Wadi Deba‘

* See relevant text for remarks on distribution in this area

† Recorded herein for the first time

X

d in Israel and Sinai

recent records from Israel and Sinai, see Distribution Maps for the species

bia	Syria	Lebanon	Turkey	Caucasus; Kurdistan	Iraq	Iran
a, Hadhramaut, cat						
4,26,54,90,97	4,14,36–Damascus, 60–Homs, 74–Palmyra, 90,100–Palmyra		14,78, 80,81,90, 93,95	4,8,14	8,11,14,35, 37,52,54,59, 69,87,90, 100	4,8,11,14, 29,47,54, 87,90,95, 100
	44; Palmyra				37,44,100	?(6,44)*
	44				?44*	?*
	?recorded by many authors*	71–Beirut, 90; additional records–Dahr el Ain, Amiyun, Sin el fil, Kariye	?*			
		44,90				
uthern Arabia,						
rded by many ors	9,14,41,43,51,77,83,90, 95,100; additional records–Doummar, Soueida, Gebel Mazar, Homs-Damascus Rd.	43,90; new record–El Kah				
4,26,41,54, 50, 70, 73, 75, 76, 8,90,97,98	?*	?*				
	4,11,14,36–Djeroud, 41,67,71,77,84,90, 93–Latakieh	11–Ein Zahalte; 30,31–Beirut; 67; 71–Beirut, Nahr el Kalb	3,11,14,41, 60,78,80,81, 84,85,90,94			

REFERENCES

1 Audouin, V. (1827) 'Explication sommaire des planches d'Arachnides publiées par J.C. Savigny', in: *Description de l'Égypte*, Paris, 22:409–412, pl. 8, figs. 1–3.

2 Balozet, L. (1971) 'Scorpionism in the Old World', in: Venomous Animals and Their Venoms; *Venomous Invertebrates* (W. Bücherl and E.E. Buckley, eds.), 3:349–371.

3 Birula, A. (1898) 'Ein Beitrag zur Kenntniss der Scorpionenfauna Kleinasiens', *Horae Soc. Ent. Ross.*, 33:132–140.

4 Idem (1900a) 'Scorpiones mediterranei Musei Zoologici Mosquensis' (Russ.) Moscou, *Izv. Obshch. Lyub. Estestv.*, 98 (3) No. 1:8–20.

5 Idem (1900b) 'Beiträge zur Kenntniss der Scorpionenfauna Ost-Persiens (1. Beitrag)', *Bull. Acad. Imp. Sci. St.-Pétersbourg*, 12 (4):355–375.

6 Idem (1903a) 'Beiträge zur Kenntniss der Scorpionenfauna Ost-Persiens (2. Beitrag)', *ibid.*, 19 (2):67–80.

7 Idem (1903b) 'Bemerkungen über einige neue oder wenig bekannte Scorpionenformen Nord-Afrikas', *ibid.*, (5) 19 (3):105–113.

8 Idem (1905) 'Beiträge zur Kenntniss der Skorpionenfauna Persiens (3. Beitrag)', *ibid.*, (5) 23 (1–2): 119–148.

9 Idem (1908) 'Ergebnisse der mit Subvention aus der Erbschaft Treitl unternommenen zoologischen Forschungsreise Dr. F. Werner's nach dem ägyptischen Sudan und Nord-Uganda XIV. Scorpiones und Solifugae', *Sber. Akad. Wiss. Wien*, 117 (2; 1):121–152.

10 Idem (1909) 'Scorpione und Solifugen von Tripolis und Barka. Nach der Sammlung von Dr. Bruno Klaptocz im Jahre 1906', *Zool. Jb. Syst.*, 28:505–522.

11 Idem (1910) 'Ueber *Scorpio maurus* Linné und seine Unterarten', *Horae Soc. Ent. Ross.*, 39:115–192.

12 Idem (1911) 'Skorpiologische Beiträge. 9. *Buthus (Buthacus) spatzi* sp. n.', *Zool. Anz.*, 37 (6/7): 137–142, 3 figs.

13 Idem (1914) 'Ergebnisse einer von Prof. Franz Werner im Sommer 1910 mit Unterstützung aus dem Legate Wedl ausgeführten zoologischen Forschungsreise nach Algerien. VI. Skorpione und Solifugen', *Sber. Akad. Wiss. Wien*, 123 (1):633–688.

14 Idem (1917) 'Arthrogastric Arachnids of Caucasia, Part I. Scorpions', *Ann. Caucasian Mus.* Ser. A, No. 5 (Israel Program for Scientific Translations, Jerusalem 1964:1–170).

15 Idem (1925) 'Skorpiologische Beiträge', *Zool. Anz.*, 63 (3/4):93–96.

16 Idem (1927) 'Wissenschaftliche Ergebnisse der mit Unterstützung der Akademie der Wissenschaften in Wien aus der Erbschaft Treitl von F. Werner unternommenen zoologischen Expedition nach dem Anglo-Ägyptischen Sudan (Kordofan) 1914. XXV. Skorpione', *Denkschr. Akad. Wiss. Wien*, 101: 79–88.

17 Bonnet, P. (1945) *Bibliographia Araneorum*, 1:551, Toulouse.

18 Borelli, A. (1914) 'Contributo allo studio della fauna Libica, materiali raccolti nelle zone di Misurata e Homs (1912–1913) dall Dott. A. Andreini', *Annali Mus. Civ. Stor. Nat. Genova*, (3) 6:148–159.

19 Idem (1924) 'Missione zoologica del Dr. E. Festa in Cirenaica', *Boll. Musei Zool. Anat. Comp. R. Univ. Torino*, 39 (26):1–16.

20 Idem (1927) 'Risultati zoologici della Missione inviata dalla R. Società Geografica Italiana per l'Esplorazione dell'Oasi di Giarabub. Scorpioni e Solifughi', *Annali Mus. Civ. Stor. Nat. Genova*, 52:346–355.

21 Idem (1929) 'Scorpions du Soudan', *Ann. Mag. Nat. Hist. Lond.*, (10) 3:297–300.

22 Brulerie, C.P. de la (1875) 'Catalogue raisonné des Coléoptères de la Syrie et de l'ile de Chypre', *Annls Soc. Ent. Fr.*, (5) 5:102–106 (Voyages Diary).

23 Caporiacco, L. di (1932) 'Spedizione scientifica all'oasi di Cufra', *Annali Mus. Civ. Stor. Nat. Genova*, 55:395–408.

24 Idem (1937) 'Risultati scientifici della missione del Prof. G. Scortecci nel Fezzan e sui Tassili (1936): Scorpioni e Solifughi', *Atti Soc. Ital. Sci. Nat.*, Milano, 76:340–354.

25 Efrati, P. (1978) 'Epidemiology, Symptomatology and Treatment of Buthinae Stings', in: Handbook of Experimental Pharmacology; *Arthropod Venoms* (S. Bettini, ed.), 48:312–317, Berlin–Heidelberg New York.

26 Finnegan, S. (1932) 'Report on the Scorpions Collected by Mr Bertram Thomas in Arabia', *J. Linn. Soc. (Zool.) Lond.*, 38 (258):91–98.

27 Gough, L.H. & S. Hirst (1927) 'Key to Identification of Egyptian Scorpions', *Bull. Minist. Agric. Egypt Tech. Scient. Serv.*, 76:1–7.

28 Gueron, M. & R. Yarom (1970) 'Cardiovascular Manifestations of Severe Scorpion Sting; Clinicopathologic Correlations', *Chest*, 57:156–162.

29 Habibi, T. (1971) Liste de scorpions de l'Iran', *Bull. Fac. Sci. Teheran Univ.*, 2 (4):42–47.

30 Hemprich, F.G. & C.G. Ehrenberg (1828/1829) 'Vorläufige Uebersicht der in Nord-Afrika und West-Asien einheimischen Scorpione und deren geographischen Verbreitung, nach den eigenen Beobachtungen', *Verh. Ges. Naturfr. Freunde*, Berlin, I:348–362.

31 Idem (1829) 'Symbolae Physicae seu Icones et descriptiones Animalium Evertebratorum, quae ex itinere per Africam Borealem et Asiam Occidentalem. Animalia articulata. Arachnoidea. Scorpiones Africani et Asiatici', *Berolini ex officina Academica*: 115–126, 2 pl.

32 Karsch, F. (1879) 'Skorpionologische Beiträge I', *Mitt. Munch. Ent. Ver.*, 3:6–22.

33 Idem (1881) 'Uebersicht der europäischen Skorpione', *Berl. Ent. Z.*, 25:89–91.

34 Idem (1886) 'Skorpionologische Beiträge', *ibid.*, 30:75–79.

35 Kennedy, W.P. (1937) 'Some Addition to the Fauna of Iraq', *J. Bombay Nat. Hist. Soc.*, 39:745–749.

36 Kerville, H. Gadeau de (1926) *Voyage Zoologique d'Henri Gadeau de Kerville en Syrie (avril–juin 1908), Tome I, 2e partie: Résultats zoologiques du voyage, Liste méthodique par H.G. de Kerville, Scorpions: 71–72*, Paris.

37 Khalaf, L. (1962) 'A Small Collection of Scorpions from Iraq', *Bull. Iraq. Nat. Hist. Inst. Univ. Baghdad*, 2 (4):1–3.

38 Kraepelin, K. (1891) 'Revision der Skorpione. I. Die Familie der Androctonidae', *Jb. Hamb. Wiss. Anst.*, 8:1–144.

39 Idem (1895) 'Nachtrag zu Theil I der Revision der Scorpione', *ibid.*, 22 (Beiheft):1–24.

40 Idem (1896) 'Neue und weniger bekannte Scorpione', *ibid.*, 13 (Beiheft):121–146.

41 Idem (1896) 'Scorpiones und Pedipalpi', *Das Tierreich*, 8 Lief., pp. 1–265.

42 Idem (1905) 'Die geographische Verbreitung der Scorpione', *Zool. Jb. Syst.*, 22 (3):321–364.

43 Levy, G., P. Amitai & A. Shulov (1970) '*Leiurus quinquestriatus hebraeus* (Birula, 1908) (Scorpiones; Buthidae) and Its Systematic Position', *Israel J. Zool.*, 19 (4):231–242.

44 Idem (1973) 'New Scorpions from Israel, Jordan and Arabia', *Zool. J. Linn. Soc. Lond.*, 52:113–140.

45 Linnaeus, C. (1758) *Systema Naturae*. 10th ed.:624–625.

46 Lucas, H. (1873) 'Note relative à des Arachnides rencontrés en Syrie', *Annls Soc. Ent. Fr.*, (5) 3, *Bull.*:172–173.

47 Olivier, G. A. (1807) *Voyage dans l'Empire Othoman, l'Égypte et la Perse*, Vol. 3 and Atlas, Paris.

48 Pallary, P. (1928) 'Description de quatre scorpions nouveaux de la Berbérie', *Bull. Mus. Hist. Nat. Paris*, 34:346–351.

49 Idem (1938) 'Sur des scorpions de la Berbérie, de la Syrie et du Congo', *Archs. Inst. Pasteur Algér.*, 16 (3):279–282.

50 Pavesi, P. (1885) 'Aracnidi raccolti dal conte Bouturlin ad Assab e Massaua', *Boll. Soc. Ent. Ital.*, 17:197–200.

51 Idem (1895) 'Viaggio del Dott. E. Festa in Palestina, nel Libano e regioni vicine. XIV. Aracnidi', *Boll. Musei Zool. Anat. Comp. R. Univ. Torino*, 10 (216):1–11.

52 Penther, A. (1912) 'Wissenschaftliche Ergebnisse der Expedition nach Mesopotamien, 1910. Scorpiones', *Annln Naturh. Mus. Wien*, 26 (1/2):109–116.

53 Pocock, R. I. (1894) 'Scorpions and Their Geographical Distribution', *Nat. Sci.*, 4 (27):353–364.

54 Idem (1895) 'On the Arachnida and Myriopoda Obtained by Dr. Anderson's Collector during Mr. T. Bent's Expedition to the Hadramaut, South Arabia; with a Supplement upon the Scorpions Obtained by Dr. Anderson in Egypt and the Eastern Soudan; with an Addendum: List of the Scorpi-

ons Obtained by Colonel Yerbury at Aden in the Spring of 1895', *J. Linn. Soc. (Zool.) Lond.*, 25: 292–316.
55 Idem (1900a) 'The Scorpions of the Genus *Heterometrus*', *Ann. Mag. Nat. Hist. Lond.*, (7) 6:362–365.
56 Idem (1900b) 'On a Collection of Insects and Arachnids Made in 1895–1897 by Mr. C.V.A. Peel in Somaliland with Descriptions of New Species', *Proc. Zool. Soc. Lond.*, 1900:48–63.
57 Idem (1903) 'Some Arachnida Collected by Mr. G. W. Bury in Yemen', *Ann. Mag. Nat. Hist. Lond.*, (7) 11:214–220.
58 Pohl, A. (1967) 'Zuordnung der Art *Buthus voelschowi* Werner, 1902 zum Formenkreis *Leiurus quinquestriatus* H. et E., 1829 (Arachnida, Scorpiones)', *Annln Naturh. Mus. Wien*, 70:209–215.
59 Pringle, G. (1960) 'Notes on the Scorpions of Iraq', *Bull. Endemic Diseases*, Baghdad, 3 (3–4):73–87.
60 Roewer, C. F. (1943) 'Ueber eine neuerworbene Sammlung von Skorpionen des Natur-Museums Senckenberg', *Senckenbergiana*, 26 (4):205–244.
61 Rosin, R. (1969) 'Effects of the Venom of the Scorpion *Nebo hierichonticus* on White Mice, Other Scorpions and Paramecia', *Toxicon*, 7:71–73.
62 Rosin, R. & A. Shulov (1961) 'Sound production in Scorpions', *Science*, 133:1918–1919.
63 Idem (1963) 'Studies on the Scorpion *Nebo Hierochonticus*', *Proc. Zool. Soc. Lond.*, 140 (4):547–575.
64 Schenkel, E. (1932) 'Notizen über einige Scorpione und Solifugen', *Revue Suisse Zool.*, 39 (15): 375–396.
65 Shulov, A. & P. Amitai (1959) 'Observations sur les Scorpions. *Buthus occitanus* ssp. *mardochei* var. *israelis* var. nov.', *Archs Inst. Pasteur Algér.*, 37 (1):218–225.
66 Idem (1960) 'Observations sur les Scorpions. *Orthochirus innesi* E. Simon 1910 ssp. *negebensis* nov.', *ibid.*, 38 (1):117–129.
67 Simon, E. (1872) 'Arachnides de Syrie, rapportés par M. Charles Piochard de la Brulerie (Scorpions et Galéodes)', *Annls Soc. Ent. Fr.*, (5) 2:245–266.
68 Idem (1878) 'Études Arachnologiques. 9e Mémoire. 15. Descriptions de deux genres de l'ordre des Scorpiones', *ibid.*, (5) 8:399–400.
69 Idem (1880) 'Séance du 11 Février 1880', *ibid.*, (5) 10 Bull.:29.
70 Idem (1882) 'Étude sur les Arachnides de l'Yemen méridional. Viaggio ad Assab nel Mar Rosso, dei Signori G. Doria ed O. Beccari con il R. Avviso "Esploratore" dal 16 nov. 1879 al 26 feb. 1880', *Annali Mus. Civ. Stor. Nat. Genova*, 18:207–206, pl. 8.
71 Idem (1884) 'Études Arachnologiques. 15e Mémoire. 22. Arachnides recueillis par M. l'abbé A. David à Smyrne, à Beirout et à Akbès en 1883', *Annls Soc. Ent. Fr.*, (6) 4:181–196.
72 Idem (1885) 'Étude sur les Arachnides recueillis en Tunisie en 1883 et 1884 par MM. A. Letourneux, M. Sédillot et V. Mayet, membres de la Mission de l'Exploration scientifique de la Tunisie', *Exploration scientifique de la Tunisie*, Paris, pp. 1–55.
73 Idem (1890) 'Études Arachnologiques. 22e Mémoire. 34. Étude sur les Arachnides de l'Yemen', *Annls Soc. Ent. Fr.*, (6) 10:77–124.
74 Idem (1892) 'Liste des arachnides recueillis en Syrie par M. le Dr. Théod. Barrois', *Revue Biol. Nord. Fr. (Lille)*, 5:80–84.
75 Idem (1897) 'Arachnides recueillis par M.M. Maindron à Mascate, en octobre 1896', *Bull. Mus. Hist. Nat. Paris*, 3 (3):95–97.
76 Idem (1902) 'Arachnides recueillis au cours de la Mission de MM. J. Bonnier et Ch. Pérez au Golfe Persique (mars–avril 1901)', *ibid.*, 8 (4):252–254.
77 Idem (1910) 'Révision des Scorpions d'Égypte'. *Bull. Soc. Ent. Égypte*, 1910:57–87.
78 Tolunay, M. A. (1959) 'Zur Verbreitung der Skorpione in der Türkei'. *Z. Angew. Ent. (Berlin)*, 43 (4):336–370.
79 Tullgren, A. (1909) 'Solifugae, Scorpiones und Chelonethi aus Ägypten und dem Sudan', *in* L. A. Jägerskiöld (ed.), *Results of the Swedish Zoological Expedition to Egypt*, 1901, Uppsala. Pt. 3, No. 21, A:1–12.
80 Vachon, M. (1947a) 'Remarques préliminaires sur la faune des Scorpions de Turquie', *Bull. Mus. Natn. Hist. Nat. Paris*, (2) 19 (2):161–164.
81 Idem (1947b) 'Répartition et origine des Scorpions de Turquie', *C. R. Somm. Séanc. Soc. Biogéogr.*,

24 (206): 26–29.

82 Idem (1948) 'Études sur les Scorpions', *Archs Inst. Pasteur Algér.*, 26 (2; 3; 4): 162–208; 288–316; 441–478.

83 Idem (1949) 'Études sur les Scorpions', *ibid.*, 27 (1; 2): 66–100; 134–169.

84 Idem (1950) 'Études sur les Scorpions', *ibid.*, 28 (2): 152–216.

85 Idem (1951) 'À propos de quelques Scorpions de Turquie collectés par M. le Professeur Dr. Curt Kosswig', *Revue Fac. Sci. Univ. Istanbul*, (B), 16 (4): 341–344.

86 Idem (1953) 'Contribution à l'étude du peuplement de la Mauritanie, Scorpions', *Bull. Inst. Fr. Afr. Noire*, Dakar, 55 (3): 1012–1028.

87 Idem (1958) 'Scorpionidea (Chelicerata) de l'Afghanistan. The 3rd Danish Expedition to Central Asia. (Zoological Results 23)', *Vidensk. Meddr. Dansk Naturh. Foren.*, 120: 121–187.

88 Idem (1965) 'Remarques sur quelques scorpions appartenant aux Genres *Nebo* Simon, 1878 (Diplocentridae) et *Hemiscorpion* Peters, 1861 (Scorpionidae)', *Bull. Mus. Natn. Hist. Nat. Paris*, (2), 37 (2): 308–317.

89 Idem (1965–1966) 'À propos d'un scorpion d'Israël *Nebo hierichonticus* (Simon 1872) (Fam. des Diplocentridae)', *ibid.*, (2) 37 (5): 766–767.

90 Idem (1966) 'Liste des scorpions connus en Égypte, Arabie, Israël, Liban, Syrie, Jordanie, Turquie, Irak, Iran', *Toxicon*, 4: 209–218.

91 Idem (1973) 'Étude des caractères utilisés pour classer les familles et les genres de Scorpions (Arachnides)', *Bull. Mus. Natn. Hist. Nat. Paris* (3), 140, Zool. 104: 857–958.

92 Vachon, M. & R. Stockmann (1968) 'Contribution à l'étude des scorpions Africains appartenant au genre *Buthotus* Vachon 1949, et étude de la variabilité', *Monitore Zool. Ital.* (N.S.) 2 (suppl.): 81–149.

93 Werner, F. (1902) 'Die Scorpione, Pedipalpen und Solifugen in der zoologisch-vergleichend-anatomischen Sammlung der Universität Wien', *Verh. Zool.-Bot. Ges. Wien*, 52: 595–608.

94 Idem (1919) 'Skorpione und Solifugen aus dem Amanus-Gebirge in: F. Tolg, Ergebnisse einer zoologischen Forschungsreise nach Kleinasien', *Arch. Naturgesch.*, 85 (A, 8): 141–145.

95 Idem (1934) 'Scorpiones, Pedipalpi', *Bronns' Klass. Ordn. Tierreich*, 5 (4. Abt., 8. Bu., 1–2 Lief.) Leipzig, pp. 1–316.

96 Idem (1935) 'Ueber Skorpione aus Palästina', *Zool. Anz.*, 109 (7/8): 211–216.

97 Idem (1936) 'Neu-Eingänge von Skorpionen im Zoologischen Museum in Hamburg', *Festschr. E. Strand*, Riga, 2: 171–193.

98 Whittick, R. J. (1941) 'Arachnida: Scorpiones, Pedipalpi and Solifugae Collected by the British Museum Expedition to South-West Arabia, 1937–38', *Br. Mus. Nat. Hist. Lond.*, 1 (5): 43–49.

99 Idem (1947) 'Results of the Armstrong College Expedition to Siwa Oasis (Libyan Desert) 1935. Scorpiones (Arachnida)', *Bull. Soc. Fouad 1er, Ent.*, 31: 121–126.

100 Idem (1955) 'Scorpions from Palestine, Syria, Iraq and Iran' (A multilithed paper distributed privately by H. Field, 1955, in: *Contributions to the Fauna and Flora of Southwestern Asia. Miscellanea Asiatic Occidentalis XII, Amer. Document. Inst. Microf.* No. 4612: 76–81).

101 Zinner, H. & P. Amitai (1969) 'Observations on Hibernation of *Compsobuthus acutecarinatus* E. Sim. and C. *schmiedeknechti* Vachon (Scorpionidea, Arachnida) in Israel', *Israel J. Zool.*, 18: 41–47.

102 Zlotkin, E. (1973) 'Chemistry of Animal Venoms', *Experientia*, 29: 1453–1466.

103 Zlotkin, E., N. Lebovits & A. Shulov (1972) 'Toxic Effects of the Venom of the Scorpion *Scorpio maurus palmatus* (Scorpionidae)', *Rivista di Parassitologia*, 33 (3): 237–243.

104 Zlotkin, E., F. Miranda & H. Rochat (1978) 'Chemistry and Pharmacology of Buthinae Scorpion Venoms', in: Handbook of Experimental Pharmacology; *Arthropod Venoms* (S. Bettini, ed.), 48: 317–369, Berlin–Heidelberg–New York.

INDEX

Synonyms in italics. The principle reference to each valid name in bold type.

Index

Index

MAP

Geographical Areas in Israel and Sinai

KEY

1. Upper Galilee
2. Lower Galilee
3. Carmel Ridge
4. Northern Coastal Plain
5. Valley of Yizre‘el
6. Samaria
7. Jordan Valley and Southern Golan
8. Central Coastal Plain
9. Southern Coastal Plain
10. Foothills of Judea
11. Juean Hills
12. Judean Desert
13. Dead Sea Area
14. ‘Arava Valley
15. Northern Negev
16. Southern Negev
17. Central Negev
18. Golan Heights
19. Mount Hermon
20. Northern Sinai
21. Central Sinai Foothills
22. Sinai Mountains
23. Southwestern Sinai

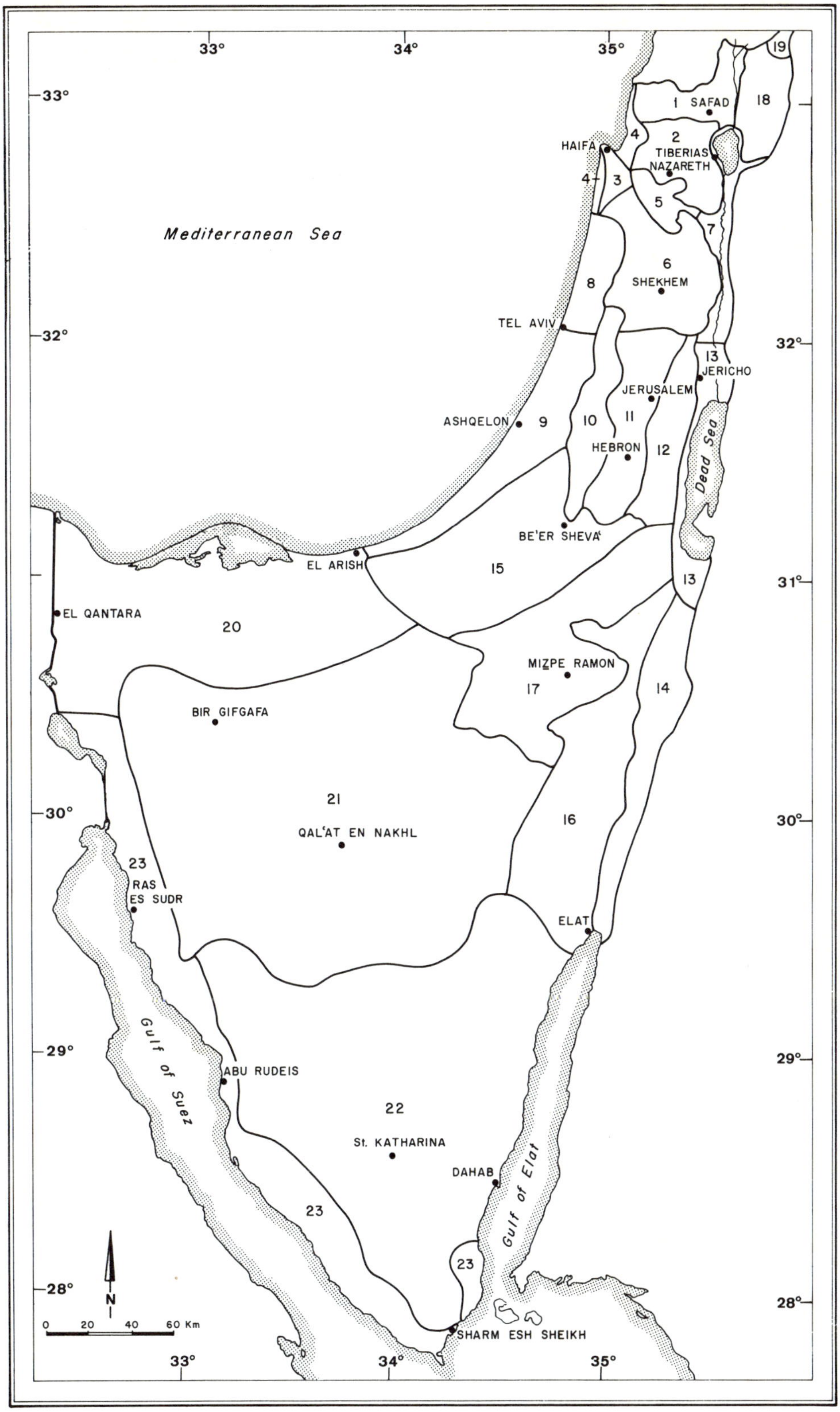

33°
34°
35°
Mediterranean Sea
1 SAFAD
2 TIBERIAS
NAZARETH
HAIFA
3
4
5
6 SHEKHEM
7
8
9 ASHQELON
10
11 JERUSALEM
12 HEBRON
13 JERICHO
Dead Sea
TEL AVIV
BE'ER SHEVA'
EL ARISH
15
13
14
16
17 MIZPE RAMON
18
19
20 EL QANTARA
21 BIR GIFGAFA
QAL'AT EN NAKHL
ELAT
22 St. KATHARINA
23 RAS ES SUDR
ABU RUDEIS
DAHAB
Gulf of Suez
Gulf of Elat
23
23
SHARM ESH SHEIKH
N
0 20 40 60 Km
33°
32°
31°
30°
29°
28°

כתבי האקדמיה הלאומית הישראלית למדעים

החטיבה למדעי־הטבע

החי של ארץ־ישראל

עכבישניים 1: עקרבים
(SCORPIONES)

מאת

ג׳ לוי · פ׳ אמתי

ירושלים תש״ם